SCHOLASTIC

Terms and conditions

IMPORTANT – PERMITTED USE AND WARNINGS – READ CAREFULLY BEFORE USING

IF YOU ACCEPT THE ABOVE CONDITIONS YOU MAY PROCEED TO USE THE CD-ROM.

Recommended system requirements:

- Windows: XP (Service Pack 3), Vista (Service Pack 2) or Windows 7 with 2.33GHz processor
- Mac: OS 10.6 to 10.8 with Intel Core™ Duo processor
- 1GB RAM (recommended)
- 1024 x 768 Screen resolution
- CD-ROM drive (24x speed recommended)
- 16-bit sound card
- Microsoft Word

For all technical support queries, please phone Scholastic Customer Services on 0845 6039091.

SCHOLASTIC

Book End, Range Road, Witney, Oxfordshire, OX29 0YD

www.scholastic.co.uk

© 2013, Scholastic Ltd

1 2 3 4 5 6 7 8 9   3 4 5 6 7 8 9 0 1 2

British Library Cataloguing-in-Publication Data
A catalogue record for this book is available from the
British Library.

ISBN 978-1407-12841-2
Printed by Bell & Bain Ltd, Glasgow

Due to the nature of the web we cannot guarantee
the content or links of any site mentioned. We strongly
recommend that teachers check websites before using
them in the classroom.

Contributors
Catherine Baker and Rosie Huckle

Editorial team
Rachel Morgan, Pollyanna Poulter and Jenny Wilcox

Cover Design
Andrea Lewis

Design Team
Sarah Garbett, Shelley Best and Andrea Lewis

Contents

Introduction

This planning guide is designed to help support schools, subject coordinators and teachers to navigate the 2014 Curriculum and to plan their school curriculum appropriately. It is now a requirement for all schools to publish their school curriculum online, and this handy planning guide can help you achieve that for the new curriculum.

The curriculum documentation for science provides a single-year programme of study for each year from Year 1 to Year 6. *Schools are, however, only required to teach the relevant programme of study by the end of the key stage. Within each key stage, schools therefore have flexibility to introduce content earlier or later than set out in the programme of study. In addition, schools can introduce key stage content during an earlier key stage if appropriate.* This new approach to providing a school science curriculum can be a complex task to ensure that a progressive and appropriate curriculum is followed in all year groups. This planning guide aims to support you in this challenge.

The aims of the 2014 Curriculum for science are embedded throughout the '100 Science' programme. These aims are to ensure that all children:

- develop **scientific knowledge** and **conceptual understanding** through the specific disciplines of biology, chemistry and physics
- develop an understanding of the **nature, processes and methods of science** through different types of science enquiries that help them to answer scientific questions about the world around them
- are equipped with the scientific knowledge required to understand the uses and implications of science, today and for the future.

In this planning guide the tables show the objectives, curriculum objectives and 'working scientifically' elements that are addressed each week throughout the year to help you begin to plan your own curriculum in science. It should be noted that as specified in the curriculum, 'working scientifically' has been 'embedded' within the scientific content of the programme rather than it being presented as a separate strand. The curriculum for each year has also been divided up into six half term 'units' of six weeks duration. Each of these units covers work in a domain (see terminology below) for that year.

Terminology

The curriculum terminology has changed; the main terms used are:

- **Domains:** the area of the subject; for science the domains are 'Plants', 'Animals, including humans' and so on.
- **Curriculum objectives:** These are the statutory programme of study statements or objectives.

■SCHOLASTIC

About the book

The book provides content for each year group (Years 1–6) and includes:

- **Long-term planning:** The overview of the domains and what should be covered in that year. These are based upon the non-statutory guidance from the curriculum.
- **Progression:** This is a year-by-year overview of how the children progress through the domains. The progression overview includes what children should already know from the previous year, what is covered in the current year and how this progresses into the following year.
- **Medium-term planning:** Six half-termly grids are provided for each year group. Each contains an overview of each week's planning including the theme being covered, the outcomes for that week and the curriculum objectives covered. Please note that due to space some of the curriculum objectives have been abbreviated to fit, we recommend that you always refer to the full curriculum documentation in conjunction with the planning guide.
- **Background knowledge:** This explains key concepts relevant to the year group to help support teacher's knowledge with the more technical curriculum coverage of grammar.

The final four pages of the book show a summary of progression and coverage for the six years through:

- biology
- chemistry
- physics
- working scientifically (although this should not be taught as a separate strand).

About the CD-ROM

The CD-ROM provides the long-term planning, progression, medium-term planning and background knowledge as editable Word files. These can be used and adapted to meet the needs of your school.

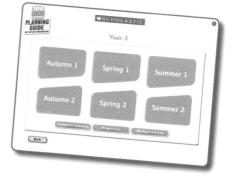

There is a simple menu screen on the CD-ROM, simply navigate to the year group you require and then click on the button to open the related file.

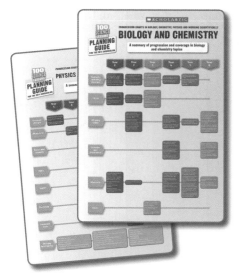

About the poster

The poster summarises some of the key features of progression for biology, chemistry, physics and working scientifically. Display it in a central location, such as the staffroom, to help improve knowledge of the new curriculum within your school.

Year 1 Long-term planning

Working scientifically

- Children should explore the world around them and raise their own questions. They should experience different types of scientific enquiries, including practical activities, and begin to recognise ways in which they might answer scientific questions. They should use simple features to compare objects, materials and living things and, with help, decide how to sort and group them, observe changes over time, and, with guidance, they should begin to notice patterns and relationships. They should ask people questions and use simple secondary sources to find answers. They should use simple measurements and equipment (e.g. hand lenses, egg timers) to gather data, carry out simple tests, record simple data, and talk about what they have found out and how they found it out. With help, they should record and communicate their findings in a range of ways and begin to use simple scientific language.
- These opportunities for working scientifically should be provided across Years 1 and 2 so that the expectations in the programme of study can be met by the end of Year 2. Children are not expected to cover each aspect for every area of study.

Plants

- Children should use the local environment throughout the year to explore and answer questions about plants growing in their habitat. Where possible, they should observe the growth of flowers and vegetables that they have planted.
- They should become familiar with common names of flowers, examples of deciduous and evergreen trees, and plant structures (including *leaves, flowers (blossom), petals, fruit, roots, bulb, seed, trunk, branches, stem*).
- Children might work scientifically by: observing closely, perhaps using magnifying glasses, and comparing and contrasting familiar plants; describing how they were able to identify and group them, and drawing diagrams showing the parts of different plants and trees. Children might keep records of how plants have changed over time, for example the leaves falling off trees and buds opening; and compare and contrast what they have found out about different plants.

Animals, including humans

- Children should use the local environment throughout the year to explore and answer questions about animals in their habitat. They should understand how to take care of animals taken from their local environment and the need to return them safely after study. Children should become familiar with the common names of some fish, amphibians, reptiles, birds and mammals, including those that are kept as pets.
- Children should have plenty of opportunities to learn the names of the main body parts (including *head, neck, arms, elbows, legs, knees, face, ears, eyes, hair, mouth, teeth*) through games, actions, songs and rhymes.
- Children might work scientifically by: using their observations to compare and contrast animals at first hand or through videos and photographs, describing how they identify and group them; grouping animals according to what they eat; and using their senses to compare different textures, sounds and smells.

Everyday materials

- Children should explore, name, discuss and raise and answer questions about everyday materials so that they become familiar with the names of materials and properties such as: *hard/soft; stretchy/stiff; shiny/dull; rough/smooth; bendy/not bendy; waterproof/not waterproof; absorbent/not absorbent; opaque/transparent.* Children should explore and experiment with a wide variety of materials, not only those listed in the programme of study, but including for example: brick, paper, fabrics, elastic, foil.
- Children might work scientifically by: performing simple tests to explore questions, for example: *What is the best material for an umbrella? ... for lining a dog basket? ... for curtains? ... for a bookshelf? ... for a gymnast's leotard?*

Seasonal changes

- Children should observe and talk about changes in the weather and the season. Children should observe and talk about changes in the weather and the season.
- **Note:** Children should be warned that it is not safe to look directly at the Sun, even when wearing dark glasses.
- Children might work scientifically by: making tables and charts about the weather; and making displays of what happens in the world around them, including day length, as the seasons change.

Overview of progression in Year 1

Working scientifically

In Key Stages 1 and 2, children will progressively develop their knowledge and experience of scientific methods and skills. The foundations for this are laid in Year 1, building on children's earlier explorations of the world around them in the Early Years Foundation Stage. Children will begin to learn how to work scientifically by applying basic methods and skills to the topics they study. The concept of working scientifically is introduced in a very natural way, as children make observations and ask questions about what they observe. They may begin to use some simple scientific equipment to help them observe closely, learn how to conduct simple tests and start to record the data gathered using simple tables and lists. They will use the results of their tests and their observations to help them work out the answers to their questions. Children will learn how to identify different members of a class of objects and how to differentiate and classify objects – skills they will go on to develop in Year 2, where there will also be a greater emphasis on recording their results.

Plants

Children will learn the names and features of a range of common plants, including trees and flowering plants. Ideally they will have the opportunity for hands-on experience and observation of plants which they are helping to grow themselves. They will become familiar with, and will compare, the different parts of plants, including trunk/stem, branches, leaves, roots, flowers, petals, seeds, bulbs and fruit. Children will practise working scientifically when they make close observations of plants, draw and label the different parts of plants, and record how plants change over time. They will build on this work when they continue their study of plants and differences between living, non-living and dead things, in Year 2.

Animals, including humans

Children will practise working scientifically as they study animals in the local environment, including different types of birds and mammals, and a range of other animals such as fish, amphibians and reptiles. They will also learn about pet animals. Through practical experience they will find out about how to care for animals, and they will learn the names of a wide range of animals. They will compare and contrast different types of animals, grouping them in different ways (e.g. carnivores, herbivores and omnivores). Children will learn about the main parts of the human body, and draw and label pictures of different body parts. They will focus on the senses, the body parts associated with each, and do a range of practical experiments and explorations using their senses. This work will be extended in Year 2 when they continue their study of animals and habitats.

Everyday materials

Children will explore a range of different materials, learning the names of them and identifying the key properties of each. They will practise working scientifically when they take part in simple experiments and tests to identify and compare the properties of materials, and find out how some materials can change shape when squashed, bent, stretched etc. They will build on this work in Year 2, when they learn more about the uses of everyday materials.

Seasonal changes

Children will learn about the weather and how it changes with the seasons. They will make some direct observations of the changing day length throughout the year and work scientifically to observe and record seasonal changes in plants and the environment around them. They could also think about what seasonal changes mean for animals. Their work on the Sun will help support their understanding of Light which is introduced in Year 3.

Medium-term planning Autumn 1: Autumn and winter

W	Outcomes	Curriculum objectives	Working scientifically
1	• To recognise changes to the natural environment that happen in autumn. • To observe changes across the seasons. • To name the seasons and their order. • To link the months of the year to the relevant season. • To identify characteristics of each season.	• To observe changes across the four seasons (autumn/winter).	• To ask simple questions. • To observe closely, using simple equipment. • To identify and classify.
2	• To observe shadows. • To measure and record shadows over the course of a day. • To describe how shadows change in shape and size over the course of a day. • To create a timeline of a day between sunrise and sunset. • To relate the apparent position of the Sun to the time of day. • To relate shadow size to time of day. • To observe and identify differences between day and night. • To compare light and dark in summer and autumn evenings.	• To observe and describe weather associated with the seasons and how day length varies.	• To ask simple questions. • To observe closely, using simple equipment. • To identify and classify.
3	• To consider how to measure rainfall accurately. • To record rainfall on a regular basis using a rain gauge. • To observe signs of wind and identify differing wind strengths. • To create a weather vane. • To identify which way the wind is blowing from the evidence of their weather vane.	• To observe and describe weather associated with the seasons.	• To ask simple questions. • To observe closely, using simple equipment. • To identify and classify.
4	• To carry out an investigation into temperatures indoors and outdoors. • To make simple temperature recordings. • To identify some nocturnal animals and consider why they are nocturnal. • To observe the leaves of some deciduous trees.	• To observe and describe weather associated with the seasons and how day length varies.	• To ask simple questions. • To observe closely, using simple equipment. • To identify and classify.
5	• To compare weather between the different seasons. • To explain why specific clothing is suited to different seasons. • To consider how animals cope with cold winter weather. • To investigate the concept of bird/animal migration.	• To observe and describe weather associated with the seasons. • To observe changes across the four seasons (autumn/winter).	• To ask simple questions. • To observe closely, using simple equipment. • To identify and classify.
6	• To observe seasonal changes in the park. • To observe one tree in detail. • To identify the characteristics of an evergreen tree.	• To observe changes across the four seasons (autumn/winter).	• To ask simple questions. • To observe closely, using simple equipment. • To identify and classify.
Assess and review		• Revision and assessment of the half term's work.	

Medium-term planning Autumn 2: Animals, inc. humans

W	Outcomes	Curriculum objectives	Working scientifically
1	• To elicit children's ideas on how our bodies work. • To know the main parts of the human body. • To understand the link between taste and the mouth/tongue. • To identify some familiar foods by taste. • To know we smell with our nose and to identify some familiar smells.	• To identify, name, draw and label the basic parts of the human body and say which part is associated with each sense.	• To ask simple questions. • To observe closely, using simple equipment. • To identify and classify.
2	• To know we hear with our ears. • To identify a variety of sounds. • To know we see with our eyes. • To know the skin is sensitive to touch.	• To identify, name, draw and label the basic parts of the human body and say which part is associated with each sense.	• To ask simple questions. • To observe closely, using simple equipment.
3	• To know and name some common animals. • To know and name the main external parts of mammals. • To know that different animals rely on different food sources to stay alive.	• To identify and name a variety of common animals including fish, amphibians, reptiles, birds and mammals. • To describe and compare the structure of a variety of common animals. • To identify and name a variety of common animals that are carnivores, herbivores and omnivores.	• To ask simple questions. • To observe closely, using simple equipment. • To identify and classify.
4	• To know and name some common birds. • To know the main external parts of birds. • To know some varieties of fish.	• To identify and name a variety of common birds and fish. • To describe and compare the structure of a variety of common birds.	• To ask simple questions. • To observe closely, using simple equipment. • To identify and classify.
5	• To know the main external parts of fish. • To know some common amphibians. • To know and name the main external parts of amphibians.	• To describe and compare the structure of a variety of common animals. • To identify and name a variety of common animals including fish, amphibians, reptiles, birds and mammals.	• To ask simple questions. • To observe closely, using simple equipment. • To identify and classify.
6	• To know and name some common reptiles. • To know the main external parts of reptiles. • To know and name some common invertebrates. • To know the main features of invertebrates.	• To identify and name a variety of common reptiles. • To describe and compare the structure of a variety of common animals.	• To ask simple questions. • To observe closely, using simple equipment. • To identify and classify.
Assess and review	• Revision and assessment of the half term's work.		

Medium-term planning Spring 1: Winter and spring

W	Outcomes	Curriculum objectives	Working scientifically
1	• To review knowledge of the natural environment. • To observe the natural environment and note seasonal changes. • To compare seasonal changes in winter with autumn. • To observe and record changes in temperatures. • To compare temperatures in different places. • To know that there is less daylight in winter.	• To observe changes across the four seasons. • To observe and describe weather associated with the seasons and how day length varies.	• To ask simple questions. • To observe closely, using simple equipment. • To identify and classify.
2	• To know that temperatures are lower outside in winter. • To know that smooth surfaces slide on ice and snow. • To know that icy weather can be dangerous. • To observe the structure of a snowflake. • To know that snowflakes are a feature of winter weather.	• To observe and describe weather associated with the seasons.	• To ask simple questions. • To observe closely, using simple equipment. • To identify and classify.
3	• To know that wintery weather can make it hard for animals to find food. • To know that animal footprints are visible in snow.	• To observe and describe weather associated with the seasons.	• To identify and classify. • To observe closely, using simple equipment.
4	• To know that animals have ways of staying warm in winter. • To perform a simple test using a thermometer to investigate insulation. • To know that some animals sleep during the winter months. • To identify some animals that hibernate and understand why they hibernate. • To measure and record weather conditions.	• To observe and describe weather associated with the seasons (winter/spring). • To observe changes across the four seasons (winter/spring).	• To ask simple questions. • To observe closely, using simple equipment. • To perform simple tests.
5	• To observe the apparent movement of the Sun. • To create models showing the movement of the Sun. • To understand the position of the Sun at different times of day. • To recognise that spring follows winter. • To know that plants begin to grow as winter ends.	• To observe how day length varies. • To observe changes across the four seasons.	• To ask simple questions. • To observe closely, using simple equipment.
6	• To identify and record signs of spring. • To compare spring with winter and autumn. • To suggest seasonal changes that may have happened to a tree. • To identify different weather conditions in different seasons.	• To observe changes across the four seasons (winter/spring).	• To observe closely, using simple equipment. • To identify and classify.
Assess and review		• Revision and assessment of the half term's work.	

Medium-term planning Spring 2: Plants

W	Outcomes	Curriculum objectives	Working scientifically
1	• To elicit children's ideas on the different plants in the environment. • To know some names of common flowering plants. • To know the main parts of a flowering plant. • To know and compare some names of common garden flowering plants. • To know some names of common wild flowering plants.	• To identify and describe the basic structure of a variety of common flowering plants, including trees. • To identify and name a variety of common wild and garden plants, including deciduous and evergreen trees.	• To ask simple questions. • To observe closely, using simple equipment. • To identify and classify.
2	• To know that flowering plants grow from seeds and have roots. • To know the basic structure of a plant. • To know that some flowering plants grow from bulbs. • To observe and record the growth of a hyacinth bulb.	• To identify and describe the basic structure of a variety of common flowering plants, including trees.	• To ask simple questions. • To observe closely, using simple equipment. • To identify and classify.
3	• To understand that plants grow from seeds. • To compare seeds from different plants. • To recognise the conditions needed for germination. • To observe and record the germination of seeds. • To observe and record plant growth under different conditions. • To understand that plants need light for healthy growth. • To understand why plants have flowers. • To suggest why flowers are sometimes scented and colourful.	• To identify and describe the basic structure of a variety of common flowering plants, including trees.	• To ask simple questions. • To observe closely, using simple equipment. • To identify and classify.
4	• To observe and compare the roots of two different plants. • To observe and record the roots of root vegetables. • To observe, record and understand the conditions needed for plant growth. • To identify different parts of plants. • To identify which part of a plant various vegetables come from.	• To identify and describe the basic structure of a variety of common flowering plants, including trees.	• To ask simple questions. • To observe closely, using simple equipment. • To identify and classify.
5	• To know some names of common trees. • To distinguish between evergreen and deciduous trees.	• To identify and name a variety of common deciduous and evergreen trees.	• To ask simple questions. • To observe closely, using simple equipment. • To identify and classify.
6	• To know that plants grow and change and that some roots, stems, flowers and leaves are edible. • To know that different plants live in different conditions. • To observe willow plants.	• To identify and describe the basic structure of a variety of common flowering plants. • To identify and name a variety of common plants.	• To ask simple questions. • To observe closely, using simple equipment. • To identify and classify.
Assess and review		• Revision and assessment of the half term's work.	

Medium-term planning Summer 1: Spring and summer

W	Outcomes	Curriculum objectives	Working scientifically
1	• To know that farmers do different jobs depending on the season. • To know that animals have young that grow and change. • To know that chickens grow and change.	• To observe changes across the four seasons (spring/summer).	• To ask simple questions. • To observe closely, using simple equipment. • To identify and classify.
2	• To know that birds build nests in which to lay eggs in spring. • To know that the Sun is low in the sky in early morning/evening. • To know that there are activities which require daylight/sunshine.	• To observe changes across the four seasons (spring/summer). • To observe and describe weather associated with the seasons and how day length varies.	• To ask simple questions. • To observe closely, using simple equipment. • To identify and classify.
3	• To know that shadows move and change as the Sun appears to move across the sky. • To know that it is important to take precautions in the Sun. • To know that the Sun appears to move across the sky during the day.	• To observe and describe weather associated with the seasons and how day length varies.	• To ask simple questions. • To observe closely, using simple equipment. • To identify and classify.
4	• To know how to observe the strength and direction of the wind. • To know how to observe and record the amount of cloud cover. • To know that rainbows can occur when the sun shines through raindrops after a shower.	• To observe and describe weather associated with the seasons and how day length varies.	• To ask simple questions. • To observe closely, using simple equipment. • To identify and classify.
5	• To know how shadows change over the course of the day and over the course of the year. • To know that the weather is generally warmer in late spring/summer. • To know that day length is longer in spring/summer than autumn/winter. • To know how day length varies.	• To observe changes across the four seasons (spring/summer). • To observe and describe weather associated with the seasons and how day length varies.	• To ask simple questions. • To observe closely, using simple equipment. • To identify and classify.
6	• To know that the environment is affected by seasonal change. • To know some changes associated with autumn, winter, spring and summer.	• To observe changes across the four seasons.	• To ask simple questions. • To observe closely, using simple equipment. • To identify and classify.
Assess and review		• Revision and assessment of the half term's work.	

Medium-term planning Summer 2: Everyday materials

W	Outcomes	Curriculum objectives	Working scientifically
1	• To distinguish between an object and the material from which it is made. • To observe a manufacturing process. • To observe the stages required to make a packed lunch. • To identify and name a variety of everyday materials. • To describe some of the properties of different materials.	• To distinguish between an object and the material from which it is made. • To identify and name a variety of everyday materials.	• To ask simple questions. • To observe closely, using simple equipment. • To identify and classify.
2	• To identify and name a variety of everyday materials. • To sort objects according to material. • To think about why an object is made from a particular material. • To identify the materials objects are made from and why each of the different materials has been chosen. • To learn why certain materials would be inappropriate for certain objects.	• To identify and name a variety of everyday materials, including wood, plastic, glass, metal, water, and rock.	• To ask simple questions. • To observe closely, using simple equipment. • To identify and classify.
3	• To know that some materials are changed in shape by forces. • To know that materials have different textures. • To identify the materials used in making certain objects and why each material has been chosen. • To learn why certain materials would be inappropriate for certain objects.	• To describe the simple physical properties of a variety of everyday materials.	• To ask simple questions. • To observe closely, using simple equipment. • To identify and classify.
4	• To explore the properties of magnets. • To test objects to see whether they are magnetic or not. • To compare all the magnetic items and discover what they have in common. • To distinguish between shiny and dull materials.	• To describe the simple physical properties of a variety of everyday materials. • To compare and group together a variety of everyday materials on the basis of their simple physical properties.	• To ask simple questions. • To observe closely, using simple equipment. • To identify and classify.
5	• To know that some materials are waterproof. • To sort materials according to whether they are hard or soft, rigid or flexible, bendy or stretchy.	• To describe the simple physical properties of a variety of everyday materials. • To compare and group together a variety of everyday materials on the basis of their simple physical properties.	• To ask simple questions. • To observe closely, using simple equipment. • To identify and classify.
6	• To know that some materials are absorbent. • To compare old and new bicycle tyres. • To think about desirable properties of bedroom curtains.	• To describe the simple physical properties of a variety of everyday materials. • To compare and group together a variety of everyday materials on the basis of their simple physical properties.	• To ask simple questions. • To observe closely, using simple equipment. • To identify and classify.
Assess and review		• Revision and assessment of the half term's work.	

Background knowledge

In Year 1, the science curriculum builds on the hands-on observational work and exploration of the world around them, which children began in the Early Years Foundation Stage. The concepts of scientific skills and methods, and what it means to work scientifically, are gradually introduced in the context of the topics children work on during the year, and children are encouraged to consider changes that happen over time. This means that new scientific concepts can be introduced in an intuitive way. Many of the concepts introduced in Year 1 will be reinforced in Year 2 in order to make sure that children are really secure in their understanding before they move into Key Stage 2.

Introducing the idea of a simple test

The concept of a fair test is formally introduced during Years 3 and 4, but the observations and mini-experiments children undertake in Key Stage 1 will help them prepare for this. It's therefore important to make sure that the children's observations and tests in Year 1 fulfil the criteria for a fair test as much as possible, and that they are encouraged to start making choices about the best ways to carry out their scientific enquiries. It's helpful to be very clear with children about the reasons for their observations and mini-experiments: we do these things because they help us to find out the answers to our questions. Emphasise this by starting with a very clear question, such as *What do we want to find out about X?* This leads on to a further question: *What can we do to find this out?* For example, if the answer to the first question is, *We want to know what happens if plants don't have any water*, the answer to the second question might be: *We can take two plants and give one plenty of water, but keep the other one dry*. Children can be invited to add their own ideas about the best ways of finding the answers to their questions and the equipment that could be used. In the context of simple tests like this, children can also be introduced to the importance of observing, and of recording their observations. Children can record results and observations by taking photos, drawing and labelling pictures, keeping a pictorial diary of a process, or creating a simple chart with numbers, words or symbols. It may be helpful to explain that unless we keep a record, we could easily forget what happened – and records also help us to compare our results at different times or in different tests.

Introducing the concept of identifying and classifying things

For Year 1 children, it may be easiest to talk in terms of sorting and grouping things in different ways, asking how things are the same and different. For example, they can observe a range of mini beasts and sort and group them according to size, body shape, number of legs and so on. Or, they might produce a visual calendar of the seasons, grouping together the pictures that represent each season. It's helpful for children to work in groups to do these activities so that they get the opportunity to talk about the process and explain their reasons for putting items in different groups, thereby consolidating their understanding. This is particularly interesting when classifying objects which might belong in more than one group.

Vocabulary to introduce in Year 1

Working scientifically: *changes over time, comparing, contrasting, criteria, data/results, describing, equipment, grouping, identify, name, observations, patterns, record, sorting, test.*

Plants: *branches, bud, bulb, deciduous tree, evergreen tree, flowers, fruit, garden/flowering plants, leaves, petals, roots, seed, stem, trunk, wild plants.*

Animals, including humans: *amphibians, arms, birds, body parts, carnivores, ears, elbows, environment, eyes, face, fish, habitat, hair, head, hearing, herbivores, knees, legs, mammals, mouth, neck, omnivores, pets, reptiles, seeing, senses, smells, sounds, taste, teeth, touch.*

Everyday materials: *absorbent/not absorbent, bending, bendy/not bendy, gas, glass, hard/soft, liquid, metal, plastic, property, rock, rough/smooth, shiny/dull, solid, squashing, stretching, stretchy/stiff, twisting, water, waterproof/not waterproof, wood.*

Seasonal changes: *autumn, dark, day length, days, hours, light, months, moon, movement, shadow, spring, summer, sun, winter.*

Year 2 Long-term planning

Working scientifically

- Children should explore the world around them and raise their own questions. They should experience different types of scientific enquiries, including practical activities, and begin to recognise ways in which they might answer scientific questions. They should use simple features to compare objects, materials and living things and, with help, decide how to sort and group them, observe changes over time, and, with guidance, they should begin to notice patterns and relationships. They should ask people questions and use simple secondary sources to find answers. They should use simple measurements and equipment (for example, hand lenses, egg timers) to gather data, carry out simple tests, record simple data, and talk about what they have found out and how they found it out. With help, they should record and communicate their findings in a range of ways and begin to use simple scientific language.
- These opportunities for working scientifically should be provided across Years 1 and 2 so that the expectations in the programme of study can be met by the end of year 2. Children are not expected to cover each aspect for every area of study.

Living things and their habitats

- Children should be introduced to the idea that all living things have certain characteristics that are essential for keeping them alive and healthy. They should raise and answer questions that help them to become familiar with the life processes that are common to all living things. Children should be introduced to the terms 'habitat' (a natural environment or home of a variety of plants and animals) and 'micro-habitat' (a very small habitat, for example for woodlice under stones, logs or leaf litter). They should raise and answer questions about the local environment that help them to identify and study a variety of plants and animals within their habitat and observe how living things depend on each other, for example, plants serving as a source of food and shelter for animals. Children should compare animals in familiar habitats with animals found in less familiar habitats, for example, on the seashore, in woodland, in the ocean, in the rainforest.
- Children might work scientifically by: sorting and classifying things according to whether they are living, dead or were never alive, and recording their findings using charts. They should describe how they decided where to place things, exploring questions for example: *Is a flame alive? Is a deciduous tree dead in winter?* and talk about ways of answering their questions. They could construct a simple food chain that includes humans (e.g. grass, cow, human). They could describe the conditions in different habitats and micro-habitats (under log, on stony path, under bushes) and find out how the conditions affect the number and type(s) of plants and animals that live there.

Plants

- Children should use the local environment throughout the year to observe how different plants grow. Children should be introduced to the requirements of plants for germination, growth and survival, as well as to the processes of reproduction and growth in plants.
- **Note:** Seeds and bulbs need water to grow but most do not need light; seeds and bulbs have a store of food inside them.
- Children might work scientifically by: observing and recording, with some accuracy, the growth of a variety of plants as they change over time from a seed or bulb, or observing similar plants at different stages of growth; setting up a comparative test to show that plants need light and water to stay healthy.

Animals, including humans

- Children should be introduced to the basic needs of animals for survival, as well as the importance of exercise and nutrition for humans. They should also be introduced to the processes of reproduction and growth in animals. The focus at this stage should be on questions that help children to recognise growth; they should not be expected to understand how reproduction occurs.
- The following examples might be used: egg, chick, chicken; egg, caterpillar, pupa, butterfly; spawn, tadpole, frog; lamb, sheep. Growing into adults can include reference to baby, toddler, child, teenager, adult.
- Children might work scientifically by: observing, through video or first-hand observation and measurement, how different animals, including humans, grow; asking questions about what things animals need for survival and what humans need to stay healthy; and suggesting ways to find answers to their questions.

Uses of everyday materials

- Children should identify and discuss the uses of different everyday materials so that they become familiar with how some materials are used for more than one thing (metal can be used for coins, cans, cars and table legs; wood can be used for matches, floors, and telegraph poles) or different materials are used for the same thing (spoons can be made from plastic, wood, metal, but not normally from glass). They should think about the properties of materials that make them suitable or unsuitable for particular purposes and they should be encouraged to think about unusual and creative uses for everyday materials. Children might find out about people who have developed useful new materials, for example John Dunlop, Charles Macintosh or John McAdam.
- Children might work scientifically by: comparing the uses of everyday materials in and around the school with materials found in other places (at home, the journey to school, on visits, and in stories, rhymes and songs); observing closely, identifying and classifying the uses of different materials, and recording their observations.

Overview of progression in Year 2

Working scientifically

Children will build on the scientific methods and skills they began to learn in Year 1, as they continue to make observations of the world around them, and ask questions about what they observe. They will extend their use of simple scientific equipment, beginning to use measuring tools such as egg timers, tape measures and scales, and they will develop their data handling skills, recording data in various simple formats such as tables and lists. They will begin to think for themselves about the best way to find the answer to a scientific question, and they will become more experienced at sorting, grouping and classifying objects. This will provide children with a good foundation for the more detailed investigations, tests and data-collection which they will begin to take part in from Year 3.

Living things and their habitats

Children will begin to learn about the characteristics and life processes shared by all living things, and will think about the main differences between things that are alive, that are dead, and that have never been alive. They will show their ability to work scientifically by classifying things according to whether they are alive, dead or non-living. With help, they will learn how to explain their reasons for placing things in different categories. They will continue to build on this logical categorisation of objects in their work in Year 3. Children will begin to understand what is meant by 'habitat' and 'micro-habitat', and will study a range of different plants and animals in their local area. They will also be encouraged to compare animals in a range of habitats to see how living things depend on each other, learning about simple food chains as part of this work. They will demonstrate that they can work scientifically by recording their observations, comparing how different animals are suited to life in their habitats, and drawing and labelling a simple food chain.

Plants

Children will build on their observations and categorisation of different types and features of plants from Year 1. They will look at how plants grow, beginning with seeds and bulbs, and find out about the conditions plants need in order to grow and stay healthy. They will conduct simple comparative experiments and tests to demonstrate this, and will record their results with increasing accuracy. Children's findings in Year 2 will prepare them for a more detailed study of the conditions needed for plant growth, in Year 3.

Animals, including humans

Children will find out what humans and other animals need in order to grow and to survive. They will find out about animal life cycles, but with an emphasis on how animals grow and change as they age, rather than on reproduction. They will begin to learn about the important factors which help humans stay healthy, including exercise, a balanced diet, and hygiene. Children will work scientifically by observing animals and humans at first hand or using secondary sources, and by thinking of good questions about how animals grow and survive, and suggesting possible ways of finding out the answers to their questions.

Uses of everyday materials

Children will build on the work begun in Year 1, by learning about the different uses of specific materials such as metal, wood, plastic, glass etc. They will help to design tests and experiments to show some of the basic properties of different materials and how they can be used. They may also find out about scientists and inventors of new materials, and why their discoveries were so useful. They will work scientifically by observing, identifying and classifying the uses of different materials, both in and around the school and elsewhere in the world around them. They will continue to explore properties of materials in their work on Forces in Year 3.

■SCHOLASTIC

Medium-term planning Autumn 1: Living things

W	Outcomes	Curriculum objectives	Working scientifically
1	• To introduce the idea that we each have individual characteristics. • To consider the differences between living things (humans). • To understand their own bodies and compare characteristics.	• To explore and compare the differences between things that are living, dead, and things that have never been alive.	• To observe closely. • To use their observations and ideas to suggest answers to questions. • To gather and record data to help in answering questions.
2	• To understand the characteristics of what is living and what is not. • To understand what it means to be alive. • To understand and identify the differences between dead and never been alive.	• To explore and compare the differences between things that are living, dead, and things that have never been alive.	• To ask simple questions. • To identify and classify. • To gather and record data to help in answering questions.
3	• To understand and identify the differences between living, dead and never been alive. • To understand the similarities and differences between mammals, including humans. • To understand that living things change.	• To explore and compare the differences between things that are living, dead, and things that have never been alive.	• To identify and classify. • To use their observations and ideas to suggest answers to questions.
4	• To understand that there are differences between living things. • To look at and identify different plants. • To identify the things plants need to survive and grow.	• To explore and compare the differences between things that are living, dead, and things that have never been alive.	• To perform simple tests. • To identify and classify. • To use observations to answer questions.
5	• To know what we need to stay alive and healthy. • To know what it is that makes us human and different from other living things. • To recognise and understand the differences between mammals.	• To explore and compare the differences between things that are living, dead, and things that have never been alive.	• To ask simple questions. • To identify and classify. • To use their observations and ideas to suggest answers to questions.
6	• To understand what it means to be healthy and how we achieve it. • To know what our senses are. • To understand how essential senses are and how we use them. • To understand the importance of senses to different animals.	• To explore and compare the differences between things that are living, dead, and things that have never been alive.	• To perform simple tests. • To use their observations and ideas to suggest answers to questions.
Assess and review		• Revision and assessment of the half term's work.	

Medium-term planning Autumn 2: Animals, inc. humans

YEAR 2

W	Outcomes	Curriculum objectives	Working scientifically
1	• To reinforce the idea that there are both similarities and differences between living things. • To understand the different stages in the human life cycle. • To understand what *growth* means using themselves and their families as practical examples.	• To notice that animals, including humans, have offspring which grow into adults.	• To observe closely. • To identify and classify. • To use their observations and ideas to suggest answers to questions. • To gather and record data to help in answering questions.
2	• To understand the growth cycle of mammals including children's pets. • To understand the frog life cycle. • To understand what birds are. • To know that birds have a life cycle.	• To notice that animals, including humans, have offspring which grow into adults.	• To observe closely. • To gather and record data to help in answering questions.
3	• To consider what babies of different creatures need. • To understand the characteristics of what different adult creatures need. • To consider how all living creatures have similar basic needs.	• To find out about and describe the basic needs of animals, including humans, for survival (water, food and air).	• To identify and classify. • To gather and record data to help in answering questions.
4	• To begin to consider what we eat and what is healthy. • To understand that the food we eat can be broken down into food groups. • To understand what a healthy diet is.	• To find out about and describe the basic needs of animals, including humans, for survival (water, food and air).	• To use their observations and ideas to suggest answers to questions. • To gather and record data to help in answering questions.
5	• To understand the importance of washing their hands. • To understanding the importance of tooth care. • To understand the relationship between the food we eat and caring for our teeth.	• To describe the importance for humans of exercise, eating the right amounts of different types of food, and hygiene.	• To use their observations and ideas to suggest answers to questions. • To gather and record data to help in answering questions.
6	• To understand the importance of exercise in staying healthy. • To understand their own daily exercise activities. • To begin to understand the effect exercise has on their pulse rate.	• To describe the importance for humans of exercise, eating the right amounts of different types of food, and hygiene.	• To use their observations and ideas to suggest answers to questions. • To gather and record data to help in answering questions.
Assess and review		• Revision and assessment of the half term's work.	

Medium-term planning Spring 1: Plants

W	Outcomes	Curriculum objectives	Working scientifically
1	• To revise the names of parts of plants including flowers, stems and roots. • To introduce the idea that plants grow and change. • To understand what the parts of flowers look like. • To understand the differences and similarities between plants and animals.	• To observe and describe how seeds and bulbs grow into mature plants. • To find out and describe how plants need water, light and a suitable temperature to grow and stay healthy.	• To observe closely. • To identify and classify. • To use their observations and ideas to suggest answers to questions.
2	• To understand the importance of pollination. • To understand the process of pollination. • To begin to understand the wide variety of plants that grow in a small area.	• To observe and describe how seeds and bulbs grow into mature plants.	• To observe closely. • To use their observations and ideas to suggest answers to questions. • To gather and record data to help in answering questions.
3	• To understand that plants are important sources of food. • To consider what foods animals and birds eat. • To consider the requirements for plant growth.	• To find out and describe how plants need water, light and a suitable temperature to grow and stay healthy.	• To use their observations and ideas to suggest answers to questions. • To gather and record data to help in answering questions.
4	• To understand that plants need water to grow and stay healthy. • To understand that plants need warmth to grow. • To understand that seeds do not need light to grow, but plants do.	• To find out and describe how plants need water, light and a suitable temperature to grow and stay healthy.	• To perform simple tests. • To gather and record data to help in answering questions.
5	• To consider the differences between seeds. • To learn how potatoes, pineapples and onions begin to grow. • To observe how plants 'drink'.	• To observe and describe how seeds and bulbs grow into mature plants. • To find out and describe how plants need water, light and a suitable temperature to grow and stay healthy.	• To perform simple tests. • To use their observations and ideas to suggest answers to questions. • To gather and record data to help in answering questions.
6	• To know some of the differences between deciduous and evergreen bushes and trees. • To know that plants have a variety of leaf shapes. • To understand the different ways that plants protect themselves.	• To observe and describe how seeds and bulbs grow into mature plants. • To find out and describe how plants need water, light and a suitable temperature to grow and stay healthy.	• To use their observations and ideas to suggest answers to questions. • To gather and record data to help in answering questions.
Assess and review	• Revision and assessment of the half term's work.		

Medium-term planning Spring 2: Habitats

W	Outcomes	Curriculum objectives	Working scientifically
1	• To reinforce the idea that there is a wide range of plants and animals in the school grounds and their own gardens. • To introduce the term *habitat*. • To understand that different habitats exist in the school grounds. • To understand that there are many different habitats needed by animals.	• To identify that most living things live in habitats to which they are suited and describe how different habitats provide for the basic needs of different kinds of animals and plants, and how they depend on each other.	• To identify and classify. • To use their observations and ideas to suggest answers to questions. • To gather and record data to help in answering questions.
2	• To learn about the range of living things living in deserts and jungles. • To learn about the range of living things that live in seas and rivers in hot and cold conditions. • To find out about the insects and invertebrates living in micro-habitats.	• To identify and name a variety of plants and animals in their habitats, including micro-habitats.	• To gather and record data to help in answering questions.
3	• To understand the characteristics of a specific creature in its habitat. • To recognise which birds use the school grounds. • To know the needs of the birds using the school grounds.	• To identify that most living things live in habitats to which they are suited and describe how different habitats provide for the basic needs of different kinds of animals and plants, and how they depend on each other. • To identify and name a variety of plants and animals in their habitats, including micro-habitats.	• To observe closely. • To identify and classify. • To gather and record data to help in answering questions.
4	• To understand the different characteristics of plants living in the school grounds. • To consider the variety of living things in a pond and begin to understand their interdependence. • To consider the range of local habitats and recognise the importance of protecting them.	• To identify that most living things live in habitats to which they are suited and describe how different habitats provide for the basic needs of different kinds of animals and plants, and how they depend on each other.	• To ask simple questions. • To observe closely. • To use their observations and ideas to suggest answers to questions. • To gather and record data to help in answering questions.
5	• To understand food chains in familiar local habitats. • To understand food chains in less familiar habitats.	• To describe how animals obtain their food from plants and other animals, using the idea of a simple food chain, and identify and name different sources of food.	• To use their observations and ideas to suggest answers to questions.
6	• To understand that living creatures move through their habitats in different ways. • To understand that living things need the correct conditions. • To begin to understand how habitats can be created and preserved.	• To describe how animals obtain their food from plants and other animals, using the idea of a simple food chain, and identify and name different sources of food.	• To use their observations and ideas to suggest answers to questions. • To gather and record data to help in answering questions.
Assess and review		• Revision and assessment of the half term's work.	

Medium-term planning Summer 1: Everyday materials

W	Outcomes	Curriculum objectives	Working scientifically
1	• To revise the names of common materials, such as *wood*, *plastic*, *glass*, *metal*, *water* and *rock*. • To introduce the idea that there are many different uses for materials. • To understand that there are many different materials.	• To identify and compare the suitability of a variety of everyday materials, including wood, metal, plastic, glass, brick, rock, paper and cardboard for particular uses.	• To ask simple questions. • To observe closely. • To identify and classify. • To gather and record data to help in answering questions.
2	• To understand and recognise the wide range of different materials that we need. • To understand that different materials are used for the same things.	• To identify and compare the suitability of a variety of everyday materials, including wood, metal, plastic, glass, brick, rock, paper and cardboard for particular uses.	• To ask simple questions. • To observe closely. • To use their observations and ideas to suggest answers to questions. • To gather and record data to help in answering questions.
3	• To know that clothes are made from lots of different materials. • To know that toys are made from lots of different materials. • To know that a bicycle are made from lots of different materials.	• To identify and compare the suitability of a variety of everyday materials, including wood, metal, plastic, glass, brick, rock, paper and cardboard for particular uses.	• To use their observations and ideas to suggest answers to questions.
4	• To consider materials that help us keep warm. • To know that metals are used for many things. • To know that wood has many uses.	• To identify and compare the suitability of a variety of everyday materials, including wood, metal, plastic, glass, brick, rock, paper and cardboard for particular uses.	• To use their observations to suggest answers to questions.
5	• To know how soil is useful. • To know that mammals, birds and insects use materials. • To explore materials and suggest why they are useful.	• To identify and compare the suitability of a variety of everyday materials, including wood, metal, plastic, glass, brick, rock, paper and cardboard for particular uses.	• To observe closely. • To perform simple tests. • To use their observations and ideas to suggest answers to questions. • To gather and record data to help in answering questions.
6	• To understand that some materials are natural and others have to be manufactured. • To consider the different materials needed to make a cake. • To know that the materials need to be mixed and heated to make a cake. • To consider that if we freeze some materials they change into something else.	• To identify and compare the suitability of a variety of everyday materials, including wood, metal, plastic, glass, brick, rock, paper and cardboard for particular uses.	• To identify and classify. • To use their observations and ideas to suggest answers to questions.
Assess and review		• Revision and assessment of the half term's work.	

Medium-term planning Summer 2: Everyday materials

YEAR 2

W	Outcomes	Curriculum objectives	Working scientifically
1	• To investigate the properties of different materials. • To investigate how the shape of a material can be changed by stretching it. • To investigate how the shape of some materials can be changed by twisting, bending, stretching and squashing them.	• To identify and compare the suitability of a variety of everyday materials for particular uses. • To find out how the shapes of solid objects made from some materials can be changed by squashing, bending, twisting and stretching.	• To perform simple tests. • To identify and classify. • To use observations to suggest answers to questions. • To gather and record data to help in answering questions.
2	• To To investigate how the shape of some materials can be changed by twisting or stretching them. • To investigate how forces such as pulling, stretching, squashing and kneading can permanently change the shape of some materials. • To investigate twisting as a force to change the shape of some materials.	• To find out how the shapes of solid objects made from some materials can be changed by squashing, bending, twisting and stretching.	• To observe closely, using simple equipment. • To perform simple tests.
3	• To explore how Dunlop invented inflatable tyres and be able to explain how the pneumatic tyre/air cushioning aids comfort. • To explore how Macintosh used rubber and cloth to create waterproof clothing. • To explore how McAdam used a mixture of natural materials to change how roads were made.	• To find out about people who have developed useful new materials.	• To observe closely, using simple equipment. • To use observations and ideas to suggest answers to questions.
Assess and review		• Revision and assessment of the half term's work.	

Background knowledge

In Year 2, children will continue to gain practical experience of making observations and carrying out simple tests to find out the answers to their questions about the world around them. During this year in particular, they begin to approach their learning in terms of the data cycle, drawing on their mathematical skills to consider how best to gather, record, present and interpret their data.

Gathering and recording data

In Year 2, children will build on the work done with simple scientific tests in Year 1. Children will continue to sort and group objects, compare features, and explore changes over time, but their observations will become more detailed, using a growing range of equipment, such as magnifying glasses, tape measures, weighing scales, and so on. They will undertake simple tests to answer a more diverse range of scientific questions, and so the gathering and recording of accurate data will become more important.

As in Year 1, it's important to be clear about the reasons why children are making their observations – what question are they trying to answer, and what is the best way of finding the answer? Children's data recording could take many different forms, including detailed observational drawings, graphs and charts which help them to collect and compare data in words, numbers or pictorial symbols. Children should also be encouraged to start looking for patterns in their results – for example, plants that are regularly watered grow better. As well as recording their own observations, children will also begin to record information from secondary sources – for example, copying a simple life-cycle diagram, finding out about a particular unfamiliar habitat, or drawing pictures to represent a simple food chain.

Introducing simple scientific language

In Year 2, children will consolidate their understanding and use of the proper scientific words introduced in Year 1 to describe what they do and what they observe. They will also build their scientific vocabulary. In addition to reading these words, children should also be encouraged to spell them correctly in their written work.

If these words are introduced in the appropriate context and used consistently, children will quickly pick them up and will enjoy trying out their new scientific vocabulary!

Vocabulary to introduce in Year 2

Living things and their habitats: *adaptation, alive, carnivore, characteristics, conditions, consumer, dead, excrete, feed, food chain, grow, habitat, heat, herbivore, life processes, light, living/non-living, micro-habitat, move, ocean, omnivore, pond, producer, rainforest, reproduce, respire, respond to stimuli, seashore, sound, touch, woodland.*

Plants (as for Year 1, plus): *germination, insect pollination, nutrients, pollination, seed dispersal, wind pollination.*

Animals, including humans: *adult, baby, bacteria, balanced diet, carbohydrates, child, circulation, dairy, exercise, fats, fibre, fitness, food groups, germs, growth, healthy, heart rate, infection, life cycle, minerals, nutrition, protein, teenager, toddler, unhealthy, vitamins.*

Uses of everyday materials (as for Year 1, plus): *characteristics, classification, man-made, natural, properties.*

Year 3 Long-term planning

Working scientifically

- Children should be given a range of scientific experiences to enable them to raise their own questions about the world around them. They should start to make their own decisions about the most appropriate type of scientific enquiry they might use to answer questions; recognise when a simple fair test is necessary and help to decide how to set it up; talk about criteria for grouping, sorting and classifying; and use simple keys. They should begin to look for naturally occurring patterns and relationships and decide what data to collect to identify them. They should help to make decisions about what observations to make, how long to make them for and the type of simple equipment that might be used. They should learn how to use new equipment, such as data loggers, appropriately. They should collect data from their own observations and measurements, using notes, simple tables and standard units, and help to make decisions about how to record and analyse this data. With help, children should look for changes, patterns, similarities and differences in their data in order to draw simple conclusions and answer questions. With support, they should identify new questions arising from the data, making predictions for new values within or beyond the data they have collected and finding ways of improving what they have already done. They should also recognise when and how secondary sources might help them to answer questions that cannot be answered through practical investigations. Children should use relevant scientific language to discuss their ideas and communicate their findings in ways that are appropriate for different audiences.
- These opportunities should be provided across Years 3 and 4 so that the expectations in the programme of study can be met by the end of Year 4. Children are not expected to cover each aspect for every area of study.

Plants

- Children should be introduced to the relationship between structure and function: the idea that every part has a job to do. They should explore questions that focus on the role of the roots and stem in nutrition and support, leaves for nutrition and flowers for reproduction.
- **Note:** Children can be introduced to the idea that plants can make their own food, but at this stage they do not need to understand how this happens.
- Children might work scientifically by: comparing the effect of different factors on plant growth, for example, the amount of light, the amount of fertiliser; discovering how seeds are formed by observing the different stages of plant life cycles over a period of time; looking for patterns in the structure of fruits that relate to how the seeds are dispersed. They might observe how water is transported in plants, for example by putting cut, white carnations into coloured water and observing how water travels up the stem to the flowers.

Animals, including humans

- Children should continue to learn about the importance of nutrition and should be introduced to the main body parts associated with the skeleton and muscles, finding out how different parts of the body have special functions.
- Children might work scientifically by: identifying and grouping animals with and without skeletons and observing and comparing their movement; exploring ideas about what would happen if humans did not have skeletons. They might compare and contrast the diets of different animals (including their pets) and decide ways of grouping them according to what they eat. They might research different food groups and how they keep us healthy and design meals based on what they find out.

Rocks

- Children should explore different kinds of rocks and soils, including those in the local environment.
- Children might work scientifically by: observing rocks, including those used in buildings and gravestones, and exploring how and why they might have changed over time; using a hand lens or microscope to help them to identify and classify rocks according to whether they have grains or crystals, and whether they have fossils in them. Children might research and discuss the different kinds of living things whose fossils are found in sedimentary rock and explore how fossils are formed. Children could explore different soils and identify similarities and differences between them and investigate what happens when rocks are rubbed together or what changes occur when they are in water. They can raise and answer questions about the way soils are formed.

Light

- Children should explore what happens when light reflects off a mirror or other reflective surfaces, including playing mirror games to help them to answer questions about how light behaves. They should think about why it is important to protect their eyes from bright lights. They should look for, and measure, shadows, and find out how they are formed and what might cause the shadows to change.
- **Note:** Children should be warned that it is not safe to look directly at the Sun, even when wearing dark glasses.
- Children might work scientifically by: looking for patterns in what happens to shadows when the light source moves or the distance between the light source and the object changes.

Forces and magnets

- Children should observe that magnetic forces can act without direct contact, unlike most forces, where direct contact is necessary (for example, opening a door, pushing a swing). They should explore the behaviour and everyday uses of different magnets (for example, bar, ring, button and horseshoe).
- Children might work scientifically by: comparing how different things move and grouping them; raising questions and carrying out tests to find out how far things move on different surfaces and gathering and recording data to find answers their questions; exploring the strengths of different magnets and finding a fair way to compare them; sorting materials into those that are magnetic and those that are not; looking for patterns in the way that magnets behave in relation to each other and what might affect this, such as the strength of the magnet or which pole faces another; identifying how these properties make magnets useful in everyday items and suggesting creative uses for different magnets.

Overview of progression in Year 3

Working scientifically

Children will broaden their scientific knowledge, as well as develop the understanding of scientific methods and skills which they began to acquire in Key Stage 1. Children will continue to be encouraged to ask their own scientific questions about the world around them, and, with support, will make decisions about how best to find answers, through observations, sorting objects in different ways, carrying out simple tests and experiments, and research using secondary sources. In particular during this year, children will begin to learn how to construct a fair test. They will also build on the work done in Year 2 on data collection, using an increasingly sophisticated range of equipment to help them, including data loggers. Emphasis will be placed on recording their data using standard units and in a wider range of formats, including notes, charts, graphs and tables. They will begin to learn how to analyse their data, looking for patterns, similarities and differences in order to reach simple conclusions. They will extend this learning as they move into Year 4, beginning to use their data to help them identify new questions for research.

Plants

Building on the work done in Year 2, children will learn more about the parts of a plant, and find out about the specific functions of those different parts (in particular, the role of flowers in a plant's life cycle and the importance of the root system and stem for transporting water and providing support). They will find out more about the things plants need in order to live and grow healthily, and will compare the needs of different plants. They will work scientifically by devising and carrying out simple fair tests to identify the impact of different factors (such as light, water, fertiliser etc.) on plant growth. They will also do simple experiments to demonstrate how water travels within plants.

Animals, including humans

Children will continue the work done in Year 2 on the importance of nutrition for animals' health, by looking at the different food groups and finding out about the contribution that each group makes. They will have opportunities to compare and contrast the needs of different animals (including humans). This work will be extended during Year 4 as children learn about the digestive system and in Year 6 as they learn about the circulatory system. Finally they will explore the role of the skeleton and muscles in some animals for support, protection and movement. Children will work scientifically to group animals in different ways (i.e. whether or not they have skeletons) and compare the ways in which animals move.

Rocks

Children will devise different ways of grouping and sorting rocks according to their characteristics, and will make direct close observation of the structure of rocks and soils using tools such as hand lenses and microscopes. They will learn about how fossils occur, which will link with their work on Evolution in Year 6. Children will work scientifically by conducting their own observations of rocks in the local environment, and will use secondary sources to find out more about fossils and learn about how rocks might change over time.

Light

Children will find out how light makes it possible for us to see things. They will learn about shadows and conduct simple experiments to show how the size of a shadow is affected by the distance between the object casting the shadow and the light source.

Forces and magnets

Children will begin to compare magnetic forces (which can operate at a distance, without direct contact) with other forces, where direct contact is needed. They will learn that magnets have two opposite poles. They will conduct experiments to show how magnets attract or repel each other, depending on which poles are facing, and this will enable them to make accurate predictions of the behaviour of magnets. They will work scientifically by devising a fair test to find out the strength of different magnets and by comparing and recording the way objects move on different surfaces.

Medium-term planning Autumn 1: Forces and magnets

YEAR 3

W	Outcomes	Curriculum objectives	Working scientifically
1	• To know that forces can make moving objects go faster, change direction or slow down. • To identify pushes, pulls and twists as examples of forces in action. • To learn that the direction forces are exerted is the direction in which the force acts.	• To notice that some forces need contact between two objects but magnetic forces can act at a distance.	• To ask relevant questions. • To record findings using simple scientific language, drawings, labelled diagrams, keys, bar charts, and tables.
2	• To know that there is a force called friction that acts between the surfaces of objects. • To understand the ways of increasing the effect of friction and how this is used in everyday life. • To understand the ways of decreasing friction and how this is used in everyday life.	• To notice that some forces need contact between two objects but magnetic forces can act at a distance.	• To set up simple practical enquiries, comparative and fair tests. • To use straightforward scientific evidence to answer questions or to support their findings.
3	• To know that gravity is a force that pulls objects downwards. • To know that forces can work in opposition to gravity. • To consider the different ways in which the effect of gravity can be slowed. • To know the factors that impact on the effectiveness of a spinner.	• To notice that some forces need contact between two objects but magnetic forces can act at a distance.	• To ask relevant questions. • To set up simple practical enquiries, comparative and fair tests.
4	• To know the forces exerted by a stretched elastic band. • To know the pushes and pulls made by springs. • To know that springs are used in a variety of ways.	• To notice that some forces need contact between two objects but magnetic forces can act at a distance.	• To gather, record, classify and present data in a variety of ways to help in answering questions. • To set up simple practical enquiries, comparative and fair tests.
5	• To know that a magnet is attracted and repelled by another magnet. • To know that magnets can be tested for strength. • To know that some materials are magnetic and some are non-magnetic.	• To observe how magnets attract or repel each other and attract some materials and not others. • To compare and group together a variety of everyday materials on the basis of whether they are attracted to a magnet, and identify some magnetic materials.	• To use straightforward scientific evidence to answer questions or to support their findings. • To set up simple practical enquiries, comparative and fair tests.
6	• To investigate whether magnets will work through a range of materials. • To understand the application of magnets in navigation. • To know how to use a force meter and read the scale on a force meter. • To have a 'feel' for a force of 1N and 10N.	• To observe how magnets attract or repel each other and attract some materials and not others. • To compare and group together a variety of everyday materials on the basis of whether they are attracted to a magnet, and identify some magnetic materials. • To notice that some forces need contact between two objects but magnetic forces can act at a distance.	• To set up simple practical enquiries, comparative and fair tests. • To gather, record, classify and present data in a variety of ways to help in answering questions. • To report on findings from enquiries. • To identify differences, similarities or changes related to simple scientific ideas and processes. • To make accurate measurements using standard units.
Assess and review		• Revision and assessment of the half term's work.	

Medium-term planning Autumn 2: Animals, inc. humans

W	Outcomes	Curriculum objectives	Working scientifically
1	• To review the importance of exercise and eating the right amounts of food in staying healthy. • To consider what is meant by a balanced diet. • To know that animals have different diets.	• To identify that animals, including humans, need the right types and amount of nutrition and that they cannot make their own food; they get nutrition from what they eat.	• To ask relevant questions. • To gather, record, classify and present data in a variety of ways to help in answering questions. • To use straightforward scientific evidence to answer questions or to support their findings. • To report on findings from enquiries.
2	• To know that some animals eat only plants for food. • To know that herbivores and carnivores have observable characteristics. • To know that some animals eat only other animals for food. • To know that some animals eat both plants and other animals. • To compare and contrast carnivores, herbivores and omnivores.	• To identify that animals, including humans, need the right types and amount of nutrition and that they cannot make their own food; they get nutrition from what they eat.	• To gather, record, classify and present data in a variety of ways to help in answering questions.
3	• To know how to arrange the food in their meals into groups for growth and activity. • To know what a healthy meal is like. • To know how the knowledge of food groups can help build a healthy diet.	• To identify that animals, including humans, need the right types and amount of nutrition and that they cannot make their own food; they get nutrition from what they eat.	• To gather, record, classify and present data in a variety of ways to help in answering questions. • To use straightforward scientific evidence to answer questions or to support their findings.
4	• To know how food is digested. • To know how the blood system transports nutrients around the body.	• To identify that animals, including humans, need the right types and amount of nutrition and that they cannot make their own food; they get nutrition from what they eat.	• To report on findings from enquiries.
5	• To recognise and describe functions of different types of teeth. • To describe ways to care for teeth and gums and why tooth and gum care is needed.	• To identify that animals, including humans, need the right types and amount of nutrition and that they cannot make their own food; they get nutrition from what they eat.	• To use straightforward scientific evidence to answer questions or to support their findings. • To set up simple practical enquiries, comparative and fair tests.
6	• To know that different people need different amounts of food. • To know that food gives us energy. • To know that there is a relationship between activity and the amount of food required. • To know that some foods from different cultures contain healthy combinations of nutrients.	• To identify that animals, including humans, need the right types and amount of nutrition and that they cannot make their own food; they get nutrition from what they eat.	• To record findings using simple scientific language, drawings, labelled diagrams, keys, bar charts, and tables. • To make accurate measurements using standard units. • To use straightforward scientific evidence to answer questions or to support their findings.
Assess and review		• Revision and assessment of the half term's work.	

Medium-term planning Spring 1: Light

W	Outcomes	Curriculum objectives	Working scientifically
1	• To introduce the idea that light travels from a light source. • To know a variety of light sources both natural and manmade. • To understand the need for light to be able to see things. • To understand that light travels in straight lines.	• To recognise that they need light in order to see things and that dark is the absence of light.	• To ask relevant questions. • To use straightforward scientific evidence to answer questions or to support their findings. • To identify differences, similarities or changes related to simple scientific ideas and processes.
2	• To understand that light is reflected from objects and that shiny objects reflect better than dull objects. • To know that the sharp edge to a shadow is due to light travelling in straight lines. • To consider when shadows are formed outside.	• To notice that light is reflected from surfaces. • To recognise that shadows are formed when the light from a light source is blocked by a solid object.	• To record findings. • To ask relevant questions. • To use straightforward scientific evidence to answer questions or to support their findings. • To use results to draw simple conclusions and raise further questions.
3	• To know that a shadow is formed when sunlight is blocked by an object. • To know that light from a range of sources produces shadows. • To consider how the shape and size of a shadow varies with the position of the light source. • To consider the properties of an object needed for forming a shadow.	• To recognise that shadows are formed when the light from a light source is blocked by a solid object. • To find patterns in the way that the size of shadows change.	• To identify differences, similarities or changes related to simple scientific ideas and processes. • To ask relevant questions. • To use straightforward scientific evidence to answer questions or to support their findings. • To set up simple practical enquiries, comparative and fair tests.
4	• To distinguish between opaque, translucent and transparent materials. • To understand that shadows of objects change during the course of the day. • To understand the properties needed in a fabric to block light completely.	• To recognise that shadows are formed when the light from a light source is blocked by a solid object. • To find patterns in the way that the size of shadows change.	• To make accurate measurements using standard units. • To gather, record, classify and present data in a variety of ways to help in answering questions. • To use results to draw simple conclusions. • To record findings using simple scientific language, drawings, labelled diagrams, keys, bar charts, and tables.
5	• To know that the position of the Sun changes. • To consider the shape of the path of the Sun across the sky. • To understand that a sundial can be used to tell the approximate time of day.	• To recognise that they need light in order to see things and that dark is the absence of light. • To notice that light is reflected from surfaces. • To recognise that light from the Sun can be dangerous and that there are ways to protect their eyes.	• To record findings. • To use straightforward scientific evidence to answer questions or to support their findings. • To make accurate measurements using standard units, using a range of equipment.
6	• To know that there is a wide range of colours that can be seen. • To describe how plants and animals use colours. • To understand the use of light and colour in the local environment.	• To notice that light is reflected from surfaces.	• To use straightforward scientific evidence to answer questions or to support their findings.
Assess and review		• Revision and assessment of the half term's work.	

Medium-term planning Spring 2: Plants

W	Outcomes	Curriculum objectives	Working scientifically
1	• To know that we eat different parts of different plants. • To introduce the concept that different parts of plants have different functions. • To know that roots take up water and anchor the plant to the ground.	• To identify and describe the functions of different parts of flowering plants: roots, stem/trunk, leaves and flowers.	• To use straightforward scientific evidence to answer questions or to support their findings. • To record findings.
2	• To recognise that leaves are needed for healthy plant growth. • To understand the need for plants to have a supply of air and light to grow healthily.	• To identify and describe the functions of different parts of flowering plants: roots, stem/trunk, leaves and flowers. • To explore the requirements of plants for life and growth (air, light, water, nutrients from soil, and room to grow) and how they vary from plant to plant.	• To set up simple practical enquiries, comparative and fair tests. • To gather, record, classify and present data in a variety of ways to help in answering questions. • To use results to draw simple conclusions, make predictions for new values, suggest improvements and raise further questions.
3	• To know that too little or too much water prevents healthy plant growth. • To know that plants need a supply of nutrients for growth. • To understand that plants produce their own food. • To understand the ideal conditions that plants require for growth.	• To explore the requirements of plants for life and growth (air, light, water, nutrients from soil, and room to grow) and how they vary from plant to plant.	• To set up simple practical enquiries, comparative and fair tests. • To gather, record, classify and present data in a variety of ways to help in answering questions. • To use results to draw simple conclusions, make predictions for new values, suggest improvements and raise further questions.
4	• To understand that different species of plants have different requirements for healthy growth. • To understand the process of pollination in plants and the role of flowers in that process. • To understand that seeds can be dispersed in a variety of ways.	• To explore the requirements of plants for life and growth (air, light, water, nutrients from soil, and room to grow) and how they vary from plant to plant. • To explore the part that flowers play in the life cycle of flowering plants, including pollination, seed formation and seed dispersal.	• To set up simple practical enquiries, comparative and fair tests. • To identify differences, similarities or changes related to simple scientific ideas and processes.
5	• To know the conditions seeds need to germinate. • To understand the contribution and work of Maria Sibyella Merian in our understanding of plant life cycles. • To know how to order the life cycle of common plants.	• To explore the part that flowers play in the life cycle of flowering plants, including pollination, seed formation and seed dispersal.	• To set up simple practical enquiries, comparative and fair tests. • To report on findings from enquiries. • To record findings.
6	• To know that different plants are found in certain habitats. • To know that there are reasons for differences in the plants that grow in different habitats. • To understand the relationships between the physical aspects of a habitat and the plants living there.	• To explore the requirements of plants for life and growth (air, light, water, nutrients from soil, and room to grow) and how they vary from plant to plant. • To explore the part that flowers play in the life cycle of flowering plants, including pollination, seed formation and seed dispersal.	• To gather, record, classify and present data in a variety of ways to help in answering questions. • To use straightforward scientific evidence to answer questions or to support their findings.
Assess and review		• Revision and assessment of the half term's work.	

Medium-term planning Summer 1: Rocks

W	Outcomes	Curriculum objectives	Working scientifically
1	• To understand a range of simple properties of materials. • To introduce the concept that there are different types of rock. • To consider a range of different rocks. • To learn about the ways in which humans use rocks.	• To compare and group together different kinds of rocks on the basis of their appearance and simple physical properties.	• To report on findings from enquiries. • To ask relevant questions. • To identify differences, similarities or changes related to simple scientific ideas and processes.
2	• To know that rocks can be tested for their ease of wear. • To know that rocks can be tested for their permeability. • To know that rocks are used for particular purposes because of their characteristics.	• To compare and group together different kinds of rocks on the basis of their simple physical properties.	• To identify differences, similarities or changes related to simple scientific ideas and processes.
3	• To learn what fossils are and how they can be used to help us understand something about the past. • To know how fossils are formed. • To understand how sedimentary rock is formed. • To understand that fossil fuels are non-renewable.	• To describe in simple terms how fossils are formed when things that have lived are trapped within rock.	• To gather, record, classify and present data in a variety of ways to help in answering questions.
4	• To understand in some of the ideas of James Hutton. • To understand the relationships between different rock types. • To know that some rock is exposed due to erosion. • To understand the structure of the Earth's crust. • To understand what volcanoes are and how they are formed. • To know that igneous rocks are formed from volcanic lava.	• To compare and group together different kinds of rocks on the basis of their simple physical properties.	• To report on findings from enquiries, including oral and written explanations, displays or presentations of results and conclusions. • To gather, record, classify and present data in a variety of ways to help in answering questions.
5	• To know that soil lies on top of rock. • To know that there are different kinds of soil. • To know that rocks of different sizes can be separated through sieving.	• To compare and group together different kinds of rocks on the basis of their simple physical properties. • To recognise that soils are made from rocks and organic matter.	• To gather, record, classify and present data in a variety of ways to help in answering questions. • To ask relevant questions. • To set up simple practical enquiries, comparative and fair tests.
6	• To understand the scientific reasoning behind decisions to use particular materials in particular ways.	• To compare and group together different kinds of rocks on the basis of their simple physical properties.	• To ask relevant questions. • To record findings using simple scientific language, drawings, labelled diagrams, keys, bar charts, and tables.
Assess and review		• Revision and assessment of the half term's work.	

Medium-term planning Summer 2: Animals, inc. humans

W	Outcomes	Curriculum objectives	Working scientifically
1	• To be introduced to the fact that all animals have skeletons. • To consider how their body feels after exercise. • To know that the skeleton is made up of lots of different bones. • To know the names of the skull, ribs and spine.	• To identify that humans and some other animals have skeletons and muscles for support, protection and movement.	• To use results to draw simple conclusions, make predictions for new values, suggest improvements and raise further questions. • To identify differences, similarities or changes related to simple scientific ideas and processes.
2	• To know that the skeleton grows from birth to adulthood. • To use the data from a survey to consider bone growth. • To know that a skeleton provides support. • To know the names and location of some of the organs of the body. • To know how the skeleton protects some of the internal organs.	• To identify that humans and some other animals have skeletons and muscles for support, protection and movement.	• To ask relevant questions. • To set up simple practical enquiries, comparative and fair tests. • To gather, record, classify and present data in a variety of ways to help in answering questions. • To use results to draw simple conclusions, make predictions for new values, suggest improvements and raise further questions.
3	• To know that some animals have internal skeletons called endoskeletons. • To know that some animals have external skeletons called exoskeletons. • To understand the important role of skeletons in protecting the organs of an animal.	• To identify that humans and some other animals have skeletons and muscles for support, protection and movement.	• To ask relevant questions. • To use straightforward scientific evidence to answer questions or to support their findings.
4	• To know that we need both the skeleton and muscles to move. • To know that muscles pull on the bones to move our limbs.	• To identify that humans and some other animals have skeletons and muscles for support, protection and movement.	• To use straightforward scientific evidence to answer questions or to support their findings. • To set up simple practical enquiries, comparative and fair tests. • To report on findings from enquiries.
5	• To understand that not all animals move in the same way or at the same speed and that the skeletal structure can be a factor in this.	• To identify that humans and some other animals have skeletons and muscles for support, protection and movement.	• To gather, record, classify and present data in a variety of ways to help in answering questions. • To ask relevant questions.
6	• To understand that we use our bodies differently to move in different ways. • To consider why we are not all able to move at the same speed.	• To identify that humans and some other animals have skeletons and muscles for support, protection and movement.	• To ask relevant questions. • To report on findings from enquiries. • To To use results to draw simple conclusions, make predictions for new values, suggest improvements and raise further questions.
Assess and review		• Revision and assessment of the half term's work.	

Background knowledge

Children will have used simple scientific tests in their work at Key Stage 1, but in Year 3 this is extended so that children will explicitly encounter the concept of a fair test. In order that they can make sense of this, and use the principle to design their own simple investigations, it's important that children both understand the criteria for a fair test, and have experience of applying these to real situations. Children should also be encouraged to play a more active role in asking scientific questions and choosing the appropriate type of enquiry to find the answers.

Introducing the concept of a fair test

Children must understand that for a fair test, just one factor (also called a 'variable') is changed at a time, while other factors are kept the same. They should recognise that if more than one factor is changed at a time, a straightforward conclusion cannot be reached. In order to really grasp this, children should have lots of practical experiences. For example, as part of the 'Plants' programme of study, they could do lots of investigations into the effects of different variables on plant growth. They could then be asked to think about what might happen if more than one variable were changed at a time. For example, if three plants were given different amounts of water, but in addition one were kept in a dark cupboard, it would be impossible to tell whether the plant looked sickly because of the lack of light or because of the amount of water it was getting.

Deciding what type of enquiry will be best to answer a question

In Year 3, children should be encouraged to contribute their ideas about the best sort of enquiry to use to answer a scientific question. It would be helpful to focus their attention on the differences between questions that can be answered by direct observation or testing, and those where you would need to rely on a secondary source. So, for example, if children were learning about different food groups and wanted to find out about how each food group affected human health, it obviously wouldn't be a good idea to design an experiment in which they stopped eating a particular food group and waited to observe the effects! Instead they would need to use secondary sources such as books, websites, films etc., to find out about this. Conversely, if they wanted to find out how the size of a shadow changes when the distance between the light source and the object casting the shadow is changed, it would make sense to carry out a simple test or experiment.

Vocabulary and concepts to introduce in Year 3

Plants (as for previous years, plus): *absorb, competition for resources, function, minerals, optimum conditions, plant life cycle, plant tissues, pores (stomata), reproduction, seed formation, structure, support, well-aerated soil, well-drained soil.*

Animals, including humans (as for previous years, plus): *ankle, arteries, backbone, ball and socket joints, bone, brain, branching blood vessels, capillaries, cardio-vascular system, cartilage, collar bone (clavicle), contract, endoskeleton, exoskeleton, extensor, fibula, finger, fixed joints, flexor, foot, hand, heart, hinge joints, humerus, involuntary muscles, joints, knee cap (patella), ligaments, moveable joints, movement, muscles, opposing pairs, pelvis, protection, shoulder blades (scapula), skeletal and muscular systems, radius, relax, ribs, skeletons, skull, sliding joints, spinal cord, sternum, support, thigh bone (femur), tibia, toe, ulna, veins, vertebrates, voluntary muscles, wrist.*

Rocks: *crystalline, crystals, erosion, fossils, grains, layers (strata), molten magma, particles, permeability, permeable, physical properties, soils.*

Light: *absorb, bright, dim, emit, light beam, light sources, light spectrum, opaque, rays, reflect, reflection, speed of light, sunlight, torch, translucent, transparent.*

Forces and magnets: *air resistance, attract, compress, direction of force, faster, floating, flying, forcemeter, forces, friction, gravity, magnetic, magnetic field, magnetic forces, Newton meter, Newtons (N), non-magnetic, north pole, poles, pull, push, repel, sinking, sliding, slower, south pole, speed, streamlined, stretch, twist, water resistance.*

Year 4 Long-term planning

Working scientifically

- Children should be given a range of scientific experiences to enable them to raise their own questions about the world around them. They should start to make their own decisions about the most appropriate type of scientific enquiry they might use to answer questions; recognise when a simple fair test is necessary and help to decide how to set it up; talk about criteria for grouping, sorting and classifying; and use simple keys. They should begin to look for naturally occurring patterns and relationships and decide what data to collect to identify them. They should help to make decisions about what observations to make, how long to make them for and the type of simple equipment that might be used.
- They should learn how to use new equipment, such as data loggers, appropriately. They should collect data from their own observations and measurements, using notes, simple tables and standard units, and help to make decisions about how to record and analyse this data. With help, children should look for changes, patterns, similarities and differences in their data in order to draw simple conclusions and answer questions. With support, they should identify new questions arising from the data, making predictions for new values within or beyond the data they have collected and finding ways of improving what they have already done. They should also recognise when and how secondary sources might help them to answer questions that cannot be answered through practical investigations. Children should use relevant scientific language to discuss their ideas and communicate their findings in ways that are appropriate for different audiences.
- These opportunities for working scientifically should be provided across Years 3 and 4 so that the expectations in the programme of study can be met by the end of Year 4. Children are not expected to cover each aspect for every area of study.

Living things and their habitats

- Children should use the local environment throughout the year to raise and answer questions that help them to identify and study plants and animals in their habitat. They should identify how the habitat changes throughout the year. Children should explore possible ways of grouping a wide selection of living things. Children could begin to put vertebrate animals into groups such as fish, amphibians, reptiles, birds, and mammals; and invertebrates into snails and slugs, worms, spiders, and insects.
- **Note**: Plants can be grouped into categories such as flowering plants and non-flowering plants.
- Children should explore examples of human impact (both positive and negative) on environments, for example, the positive effects of nature reserves, ecologically planned parks, or garden ponds, and the negative effects of population and development, litter or deforestation.
- Children might work scientifically by: using and making simple guides or keys to explore and identify local plants and animals; making a guide to local living things; raising and answering questions based on their observations of animals and what they have found out about other animals that they have researched.

Animals, including humans

- Children should be introduced to the main body parts associated with the digestive system and explore questions that help them to understand their special functions.
- Children might work scientifically by: comparing the teeth of carnivores and herbivores, and suggesting reasons for differences; finding out what damages teeth and how to look after them. They might draw and discuss their ideas about the digestive system and compare them with models or images.

States of matter

- Children should explore a variety of everyday materials and develop simple descriptions of the states of matter (solids hold their shape; liquids form a pool not a pile; gases escape from an unsealed container). Children should observe water as a solid, a liquid and a gas and should note the changes to water when it is heated or cooled.
- **Note**: Teachers should avoid using materials where heating is associated with chemical change.
- Children might work scientifically by: grouping and classifying a variety of different materials; exploring the effect of temperature on substances such as chocolate, butter, cream. They could research the temperature at which materials change state, for example, when iron melts or when oxygen condenses into a liquid. They might observe and record evaporation over a period of time, for example, a puddle in the playground or washing on a line, and investigate the effect of temperature on washing drying or snowmen melting.

Sound

- Children should explore and identify the way sound is made through vibration in a range of different musical instruments from around the world; and find out how the pitch and volume of sounds can be changed.
- Children might work scientifically by: finding patterns in the sounds that are made by different objects such as saucepan lids of different sizes or elastic bands of different thicknesses. They might make earmuffs from a variety of different materials to investigate which provides the best insulation against sound. They could make and play their own instruments by using what they have found out about pitch and volume.

Electricity

- Children should construct simple series circuits, trying different components, for example, bulbs, buzzers and motors, and including switches, and use their circuits to create simple devices. Children should draw the circuit as a pictorial representation, not necessarily using conventional circuit symbols; these are introduced in Year 6.
- **Note**: Children might use the terms current and voltage, but these should not be introduced or defined formally at this stage. Children should be taught about precautions for working safely with electricity.
- Children might work scientifically by: observing patterns, for example, that bulbs get brighter if more cells are added, that metals tend to be conductors, and that some materials can be used to connect across a gap in a circuit.

Overview of progression in Year 4

Working scientifically

Children's work in Year 4 develops and extends their grasp of scientific skills and methods introduced in Year 3. Children will continue to ask their own scientific questions, and they will become increasingly independent in thinking of effective ways to answer them. Children will learn more about devising and carrying out fair tests, and about recording and analysing their data. They will learn how to look for patterns in data, including changes, similarities and differences, and with support they will learn how to explain these clearly, drawing appropriate conclusions (including considering ways of improving investigations, identifying new questions to be answered, and devising new tests to find the answers). Children will become more independent and confident using secondary sources for research, including using simple keys, and they will begin to distinguish between times when secondary sources provide the best way of finding answers, and times when first-hand observations and tests are more appropriate. Children will also become more confident and proficient in communicating their results to others, through oral presentations as well as written reports, charts, graphs, etc.

Living things and their habitats

Children will continue to observe and identify plants and animals in the local environment, and will learn how to classify animals into vertebrates and invertebrates using classification keys. They will also learn to group plants into different categories, such as flowering and non-flowering plants. As part of their study of the local environment, children will learn about how animal and plant habitats are affected by changes in the environment (both human and natural) throughout the year.

Animals, including humans

Building on their work in Year 3, children will find out more about the human digestive system, identifying the parts of the body involved and the functions performed by each part. They will focus in particular on teeth, and will learn about the roles and functions of the different types of teeth, making observations to compare the teeth of herbivores, carnivores and omnivores and discussing possible reasons for the differences. They construct and interpret a variety of food chains, identifying producers, predators and prey.

States of matter

Children will learn how to group materials according to whether they are solids, liquids or gases. They will work scientifically when they do simple experiments with water to show its different properties in solid, liquid and gaseous form. They will also look at how different materials change when heated or cooled (i.e. chocolate and butter). They will learn about the role of evaporation and condensation in the water cycle, and will do simple experiments to identify the effect of temperature on the rate of evaporation. This links to Year 5, when they will study the properties of everyday materials and the concept of reversible change.

Sound

Children will learn about how sounds are made, and through simple tests and experiments (including with musical instruments) they will notice the link between vibration and sound. They will conduct tests to explore how different factors can change pitch and volume.

Electricity

Children will learn to make a simple electrical circuit using different components, including bulbs, buzzers, motors and switches. They will record their circuits pictorially (building on this in Year 6 when they learn the conventional circuit symbols). Children will conduct observations to work out the effects of adding a switch to a circuit, and will find out how to arrange a circuit in order for a bulb to light. They will learn about conductors and insulators, and in particular that metals tend to be good conductors. They will do some simple tests to show whether different materials can fill a gap in an electrical circuit.

Medium-term planning Autumn 1: Living things

W	Outcomes	Curriculum objectives	Working scientifically
1	• To sort living things into plants and animals identifying some similarities and differences between them. • To know there are different types of non-flowering plants. • To justify own criteria used for grouping. • To develop an awareness of the importance of careful observation and recording in the life of a scientist.	• To explore and use classification keys to help group, identify and name a variety of living things in their local and wider environment.	• To identify differences, similarities or changes related to simple scientific ideas and processes. • To record findings using drawings.
2	• To understand the breadth of variety in flowering plants. • To be able to name some common flowers. • To use a simple identification guide. • To explore how local habitats change throughout the year.	• To explore and use classification keys to help group, identify and name a variety of living things in their local and wider environment. • To recognise that environments can change and that this can sometimes pose dangers to living things.	• To record findings using drawings. • To gather, record, classify and present data in a variety of ways to help in answering questions. • To identify differences, similarities or changes related to simple scientific ideas and processes.
3	• To know that animals can be grouped into those with and without backbones. • To know the five different groups of animals with backbones and their key features. • To identify local birds. • To construct a simple guide to identify local invertebrates.	• To explore and use classification keys to help group, identify and name a variety of living things in their local and wider environment.	• To gather, record, classify and present data in a variety of ways to help in answering questions.
4	• To understand how to use a decision tree to classify or identify an animal. • To develop understanding of why it is helpful to have a shared system of classification. • To make a simple decision tree.	• To explore and use classification keys to help group, identify and name a variety of living things in their local and wider environment.	• To gather, record, classify and present data in a variety of ways to help in answering questions.
5	• To find out about the key features of an animal group. • To present research on the key features of an animal group to peers both orally and through a display. • To discuss examples of how changes to habitats affect living things.	• To recognise that environments can change and that this can sometimes pose dangers to living things.	• To report on findings from enquiries, including oral and written explanations, displays or presentations of results and conclusions. • To identify differences, similarities or changes related to simple scientific ideas and processes.
6	• To consider ways to make a positive impact on the environment. • To reflect on the impact of human activity on the environment. • To begin to understand that local actions affect global environments.	• To recognise that environments can change and that this can sometimes pose dangers to living things.	• To ask relevant questions. • To gather, record, classify and present data in a variety of ways to help in answering questions.
Assess and review	• Revision and assessment of the half term's work.		

Medium-term planning Autumn 2: Animals, inc. humans

W	Outcomes	Curriculum objectives	Working scientifically
1	• To explore existing ideas about what happens to the food we eat. • To recognise that there are different types of teeth in different parts of the mouth. • To consider the link between the shape of teeth and diet.	• To describe the simple functions of the basic parts of the digestive system in humans. • To identify the different types of teeth in humans and their simple functions.	• To gather, record, classify and present data in a variety of ways to help in answering questions. • To record findings using drawings.
2	• To know the different kinds of human teeth and understand how the shape of teeth is linked to their function. • To know which foods are most damaging for teeth. • To understand why we need to brush teeth to remove plaque.	• To identify the different types of teeth in humans and their simple functions.	• To set up simple practical enquiries, comparative and fair tests. • To gather, record, classify and present data in a variety of ways to help in answering questions.
3	• To know how we can care for our teeth. • To plan and set up an investigation into the effect of different drinks on teeth.	• To identify the different types of teeth in humans and their simple functions.	• To set up simple practical enquiries, comparative and fair tests. • To report on findings from enquiries, including oral and written explanations, displays or presentations of results and conclusions.
4	• To report on findings and consider the implications for caring for teeth. • To know that we have two sets of teeth in our life. • To understand the role of the tongue in the digestive system.	• To describe the simple functions of the basic parts of the digestive system in humans. • To identify the different types of teeth in humans and their simple functions.	• To ask relevant questions. • To use results to draw simple conclusions, make predictions for new values, suggest improvements and raise further questions.
5	• To know the pathway that food takes from mouth to anus. • To consolidate knowledge of the digestive system. • To understand that the digestive system's purpose is to break down food into tiny bits. • To consider the waste products of digestion.	• To describe the simple functions of the basic parts of the digestive system in humans.	• To record findings using simple scientific language, drawings, labelled diagrams, keys, bar charts and tables. • To report on findings from enquiries, including oral and written explanations, displays or presentations of results and conclusions.
6	• To consolidate knowledge of the digestive system. • To consider the digestive system in relation to other body systems.	• To describe the simple functions of the basic parts of the digestive system in humans.	• To report on findings from enquiries, including oral and written explanations, displays or presentations of results and conclusions. • To record findings using simple scientific language, drawings, labelled diagrams, keys, bar charts and tables.
Assess and review	• Revision and assessment of the half term's work.		

Medium-term planning Spring 1: Sound

W	Outcomes	Curriculum objectives	Working scientifically
1	• To elicit existing ideas about sound. • To develop awareness of the variety of different sounds made by different sources. • To understand that sound travels out in all directions.	• To recognise that sounds get fainter as the distance from the sound source increases.	• To ask relevant questions. • To set up simple practical enquiries, comparative and fair tests. • To identify differences, similarities or changes related to simple scientific ideas and processes.
2	• To know that sounds can be made in a variety of ways. • To understand that all sounds are vibrations, even if the vibrations are too small to see. • To identify the vibrating parts of sources of sound.	• To identify how sounds are made, associating some of them with something vibrating.	• To ask relevant questions. • To set up simple practical enquiries, comparative and fair tests. • To gather, record, classify and present data in a variety of ways to help in answering questions.
3	• To recognise that sounds get fainter as you get further from their source. • To understand that sound can travel through solids. • To know that sound can be reflected from solids and this explains echoes. • To know that sound can travel through liquids.	• To recognise that sounds get fainter as the distance from the sound source increases.	• To set up simple practical enquiries, comparative and fair tests. • To gather, record, classify and present data in a variety of ways to help in answering questions.
4	• To measure volume with a data logger. • To understand the volume of sound experienced can be changed with a cone shape. • To consider how the volume of sound can be reduced by insulating materials. • To understand that volume is linked to the strength of vibrations. • To understand that dataloggers can be used to measure the volume of sound and how this changes over time.	• To find patterns between the volume of a sound and the strength of the vibrations that produced it.	• To set up simple practical enquiries, comparative and fair tests. • To make accurate measurements using data loggers. • To use results to draw simple conclusions, make predictions for new values, suggest improvements and raise further questions.
5	• To recognise high and low pitch. • To recognise that the pitch of a sound is related to length of an instrument. • To recognise that the pitch of a sound is related to the length of the vibrating part. • To consolidate understanding that the pitch of a sound is related to features of the vibrating part.	• To find patterns between the pitch of a sound and features of the object that produced it.	• To record findings.
6	• To consolidate knowledge and understanding of ways of making and varying sound.	• To identify how sounds are made, associating some of them with something vibrating.	• To ask relevant questions. • To record findings.
Assess and review	• Revision and assessment of the half term's work.		

Medium-term planning Spring 2: Animals, inc. humans

W	Outcomes	Curriculum objectives	Working scientifically
1	• To review children's ideas about living things, habitats and food chains. • To know what the terms 'habitat' and micro habitat mean. • To identify different physical aspects of habitats.	• To construct and interpret a variety of food chains, identifying producers, predators and prey.	• To ask relevant questions.
2	• To learn why animals are found in a certain habitat. • To be able to choose appropriate equipment to collect an animal carefully. • To know that animals eat certain foods in a habitat.	• To construct and interpret a variety of food chains, identifying producers, predators and prey.	• To ask relevant questions.
3	• To understand what is meant by a food chain. • To know what the terms 'producer' and 'consumer' mean. • To be able to construct food chains with two links. • To understand the terms 'predator' and 'prey'.	• To construct and interpret a variety of food chains, identifying producers, predators and prey.	• To use scientific evidence to answer questions.
4	• To understand the terms 'carnivore' and 'herbivore'. • To understand that food chains are part of more complex food webs. • To consider how local animals are adapted to their environment in different ways. • To understand that animals are in competition for resources.	• To construct and interpret a variety of food chains, identifying producers, predators and prey.	• To use results to draw simple conclusions, suggest improvements, and raise further questions.
5	• To begin to understand that humans can select characteristics to breed. • To make and record systematic comparisons. • To know that plants have main features similar to their parent plants, but there is also variation between them.	• To construct and interpret a variety of food chains, identifying producers, predators and prey.	• To set up simple practical enquiries, comparative and fair tests. • To gather, record, classify and present data in a variety of ways to help in answering questions. • To record findings using simple scientific language, drawings, labelled diagrams, keys, bar charts, and tables.
6	• To understand that different animal characteristics aid survival. • To apply understanding of animal adaptation. • To consolidate and apply understanding of how living things resemble their parents and are suited to their environment.	• To construct and interpret a variety of food chains, identifying producers, predators and prey.	• To ask relevant questions. • To report on findings from enquiries.
Assess and review		• Revision and assessment of the half term's work.	

■ SCHOLASTIC

Medium-term planning Summer 1: States of matter

W	Outcomes	Curriculum objectives	Working scientifically
1	• To consider existing ideas about water. • To group materials using different criteria. • To identify differences between solids and liquids. • To know that solids made of very small particles can be poured in a similar way to liquids.	• To compare and group materials together, according to whether they are solids, liquids or gases.	• To ask relevant questions. • To gather, record, classify and present data in a variety of ways to help answer questions. • To identify differences and similarities related to simple scientific ideas and processes.
2	• To know some common characteristics of gases. • To be able to classify materials as solid, liquid or gas. • To become aware that the same material can exist as a solid or liquid. • To clarify ideas about the characteristics of solids, liquids and gases.	• To compare and group materials together, according to whether they are solids, liquids or gases.	• To identify differences and similarities related to simple scientific ideas and processes.
3	• To be aware that everyday materials may be a mixture of solids, liquids and gases. • To know that heating can cause melting and cooling can cause solidifying. • To know that different materials melt at different temperatures. • To know that temperature is measured in Celsius (°C). • To measure the temperature of different materials.	• To observe that some materials change state when they are heated or cooled, and measure the temperature at which this happens in degrees Celsius (°C).	• To identify differences, similarities or changes related to simple scientific ideas and processes. • To make accurate measurements using standard units, using thermometers.
4	• To know the temperature in Celsius (°C) at which ice melts. • To begin to consider evaporation. • To know that evaporation is faster in warmer conditions.	• To observe that some materials change state when they are heated or cooled, and measure the temperature at which this happens in degrees Celsius (°C). • To associate the rate of evaporation with temperature.	• To ask relevant questions. • To make accurate measurements using data loggers. • To use straightforward scientific evidence to answer questions or to support their findings. • To use results to draw simple conclusions, make predictions for new values, suggest improvements and raise further questions.
5	• To understand that droplets of condensation are formed from water vapour. • To consolidate understanding of melting/solidifying and evaporation/condensation. • To consider factors affecting the rate of evaporation.	• To identify the part played by evaporation and condensation in the water cycle.	• To set up simple practical enquires, comparative and fair tests. • To gather, record, classify and present data in a variety of ways to help answer questions. • To identify differences, similarities or changes related to simple scientific ideas and processes.
6	• To consider the water cycle in terms of evaporation and condensation. • To consolidate understanding of the water cycle. • To consolidate knowledge of solids, liquids and gases and associated vocabulary.	• To identify the part played by evaporation and condensation in the water cycle.	• To record findings using simple scientific language, drawings, labelled diagrams, keys, bar charts and tables.
Assess and review		• Revision and assessment of the half term's work.	

Medium-term planning Summer 2: Electricity

W	Outcomes	Curriculum objectives	Working scientifically
1	• To elicit children's existing ideas about electricity. • To identify common appliances that run on electricity. • To know that mains electricity is a form of energy that has been converted from other forms of energy. • To know that appliances powered by mains electricity are not safe for them to investigate.	• To identify common appliances that run on electricity.	• To ask relevant questions. • To gather, record, classify and present data in a variety of ways to help in answering questions.
2	• To know how to construct simple circuits. • To develop and consolidate the idea that current travels in a circuit. • To know what is needed for a circuit to work.	• To construct a simple series electrical circuit. • To identify whether or not a lamp will light in a simple series circuit, based on whether or not the lamp is part of a complete loop with a battery.	• To set up simple practical enquiries, comparative and fair tests. • To identify differences, similarities or changes related to simple scientific ideas and processes.
3	• To construct simple circuits using buzzers and motors. • To know that current must flow though buzzers in the right direction for them to work. • To know that the direction of the motor can be reversed.	• To construct a simple series electrical circuit.	• To set up simple practical enquiries, comparative and fair tests. • To identify differences, similarities or changes related to simple scientific ideas and processes.
4	• To know that switches break a circuit and they can be made in a variety of ways. • To develop and apply knowledge and understanding of switches in model making.	• To recognise that a switch opens and closes a circuit and associate this with whether or not a lamp lights in a simple series circuit.	• To set up simple practical enquiries, comparative and fair tests. • To record findings using labelled diagrams. • To report on findings from enquiries, including displays.
5	• To become familiar with a range of different commercial switches and begin to identify their common features. • To group materials into electrical conductors and electrical insulators. • To recognise that metals are good conductors. • To develop and apply understanding of conductors and insulators.	• To recognise that a switch opens and closes a circuit and associate this with whether or not a lamp lights in a simple series circuit. • To recognise some common conductors and insulators, and associate metals with being good conductors.	• To set up simple practical enquiries, comparative and fair test. • To record findings using drawings. • To report on findings from enquiries, including oral and written explanations.
6	• To consolidate understanding of conductor and insulators and the effect of combining components in simple circuits. • To understand that the brightness of bulbs can be changed by varying circuits. • To be aware that circuits can be modelled using ICT.	• To recognise some common conductors and insulators, and associate metals with being good conductors.	• To gather, record, classify and present data in a variety of ways to help in answering questions. • To use results to draw simple conclusions, make predictions for new values, suggest improvements and raise further questions.
Assess and review		• Revision and assessment of the half term's work.	

Background knowledge

Children will gather data from a wider range of observations and tests, and continue to use more sophisticated data-gathering tools and standard units of measure. They will begin to bring their own ideas to the analysis of their data, looking for patterns and changes, and learn how to use ideas gleaned from the data analysis to identify new questions for research.

Analysing data

From experience, children will begin to recognise that whenever you do an experiment or test, you will end up with some data. They will see that some experiments produce relatively small amounts of data, whereas some experiments produce lots. Children will need guidance to understand how, as scientists, to work with this more complex data. Of course, data itself can't answer a question directly – we need to add human insights to analyse it and find out what it might mean. Children will need support to think about how best to record their data to make that analysis easier. As part of their work on habitats, children might make direct observations of the local environment across a long period, such as a month or a year. They will end up with lots of data, which might show (for example) which minibeasts they found in particular habitats on each occasion. Plotting information on a bar chart will show the frequency of particular minibeasts during each month, and should make it easier to spot any patterns emerging which would suggest further questions that they could research. Children could also think about whether the patterns they observe are clear. This will eventually lead to a more statistical approach to experimentation, for example repeating experiments to find out whether the initial results are sound. Although not required at this stage, it's helpful for children to begin to think about the reliability of data, and if they think results are believable.

Identifying new questions from data

In Year 4, children will be encouraged to identify further questions arising from the data they have collected, which might be answered by further research. They should recognise that most scientific discoveries have resulted from scientists taking this approach to their work. Although it's satisfying to create a neat bar graph of your results, this is arguably a waste of time unless you are asking what the results mean and how you can find out more. So, for example, observations of the environment might show lots of butterflies during June and July, but very few in November. Encourage the children to ask why this might be. The best way to research this would probably be through secondary sources giving information about butterflies' life cycle and the conditions they need in order to thrive. Sometimes, experiments give answers which you really were not expecting, or which don't seem to make sense. It's important for children to think about this – figuring out why your experiment might have given a nonsense result is an important part of scientific thinking.

Vocabulary and concepts to introduce in Year 4

Living things and their habitats (as for Year 2, plus): *classification keys, differences, human effects on the environment (population, development, deforestation, pollution), invertebrates (snails and slugs, worms, spiders, insects), organism, plant groups (trees, grasses, flowering plants, non-flowering plants), similarities, variation characteristics, vertebrates (fish, amphibians, reptiles, birds, mammals).*

Animals, including humans (as for previous years, plus): *absorption of food into blood stream, canines, cavities, chemical breakdown by enzymes, chewing, churning in stomach, dentine, digestion, digestive system, enamel, faeces, fluoride toothpaste, gastric juice, gums, incisors, intestine, molars, nerves, oesophagus, plaque, premolars, pulp cavity, predators, prey, producers, reabsorption of water from waste, saliva, swallowing, tooth decay.*

States of matter: *boiling, condensation, degrees Celsius (°C), energy transfer solid, evaporation, fixed shape and volume, forces of attraction, freezing, gaseous, liquid, melting, particles, rate of evaporation, solidifying, temperature, thermometer, vibrate, water cycle.*

Sound: *echo, frequency of vibration, pitch (higher, lower), reflection of sound, sound insulation, sound wave, tuning fork, vacuum, vibration, volume (louder, softer).*

Electricity: *battery, bulbs, buzzers, cell, closed circuit, conductor, crocodile clips, electrical appliances, insulator, motors, open circuit, simple series circuit, switches, wires.*

Year 5 Long-term planning

Working scientifically

- Children in Years 5 and 6 should use their science experiences to: explore ideas and raise different kinds of questions; select and plan the most appropriate type of scientific enquiry to use to answer scientific questions; recognise when and how to set up comparative and fair tests and explain which variables need to be controlled and why. They should use and develop keys and other information records to identify, classify and describe living things and materials, and identify patterns that might be found in the natural environment. They should make their own decisions about what observations to make, what measurements to use and how long to make them for, and whether to repeat them; choose the most appropriate equipment to make measurements and explain how to use it accurately. They should decide how to record data from a choice of familiar approaches; look for different causal relationships in their data and identify evidence that refutes or supports their ideas. They should use their results to identify when further tests and observations might be needed; recognise which secondary sources will be most useful to research their ideas and begin to separate opinion from fact. They should use relevant scientific language and illustrations to discuss, communicate and justify their scientific ideas and should talk about how scientific ideas have developed over time.
- These opportunities for working scientifically should be provided across Years 5 and 6 so that the expectations in the programme of study can be met by the end of Year 6. Children are not expected to cover each aspect for every area of study.

Living things and their habitats

- Children should study and raise questions about their local environment throughout the year. They should observe life-cycle changes in a variety of living things and animals in the local environment. They should find out about the work of naturalists and animal behaviourists, for example, David Attenborough and Jane Goodall.
- Children should find out about different types of reproduction in plants and animals.
- Children might work scientifically by: observing and comparing the life cycles of plants and animals in their local environment with other plants and animals around the world (in the rainforest, in the oceans, in desert areas and in prehistoric times), asking pertinent questions and suggesting reasons for similarities and differences. They might try to grow new plants from different parts of the parent plant, for example, seeds, stem and root cuttings, tubers, bulbs. They might observe changes in an animal over a period of time (for example, by hatching and rearing chicks), comparing how different animals reproduce and grow.

Animals, including humans

- Children should draw a timeline to indicate stages in the growth of humans, and learn about puberty.
- Children could work scientifically by comparing the gestation periods of other animals with humans.

Properties and changes of materials

- Children should build a more systematic understanding of materials by exploring and comparing the properties of a broad range of materials, including relating these to what they learnt about magnetism in Year 3 and about electricity in Year 4. They should explore reversible changes, including, evaporating, filtering, sieving, melting and dissolving, recognising that melting and dissolving are different processes. Children should explore changes that are difficult to reverse, for example, burning, rusting and other reactions, for example, vinegar with bicarbonate of soda. They should find out about how chemists create new materials.
- **Note**: At this stage, it is sufficient for children to observe that some conductors will produce a brighter bulb in a circuit than others and that some materials will feel hotter than others when a heat source is placed against them. Safety guidelines should be followed when burning materials.
- Children might work scientifically by: carrying out tests to answer questions, for example, 'Which materials would be the most effective for making a warm jacket?' They might compare materials in order to make a switch in a circuit. They could observe and compare the changes that take place, for example, when burning different materials or baking bread or cakes. They might research and discuss how chemical changes have an impact on our lives, and discuss the creative use of new materials such as polymers and super-thin materials.

Earth and space

- Children should be introduced to a model of the Sun and Earth that enables them to explain day and night. Children should learn that the Sun is a star at the centre of our solar system and that it has eight planets. They should understand that a moon is a celestial body that orbits a planet.
- **Note**: Children should be warned that it is not safe to look directly at the Sun, even when wearing dark glasses.
- Children should find out about the way that ideas about the solar system have developed, and understand the geocentric and heliocentric models by considering the work of scientists such as Ptolemy, Alhazen and Copernicus.
- Children might work scientifically by: comparing the time of day at different places on the Earth through internet links and direct communication; creating simple models of the solar system and so on.

Forces

- Children should explore falling objects and raise questions about the effects of air resistance. They should explore the effects of air resistance by observing how different objects fall. They should experience forces that make things begin to move, get faster or slow down. Children should explore the effects of friction on movement and find out how it slows or stops moving objects. Children should explore the effects of levers, pulleys and simple machines on movement. Children might find out how scientists helped to develop the theory of gravitation.
- Children might work scientifically by: exploring falling paper cones or cup-cake cases, and designing and making a variety of parachutes and carrying out fair tests to determine which designs are the most effective. They might explore resistance in water by making and testing boats of different shapes. They might design and make products that use levers, pulleys, gears and/or springs and explore their effects.

Overview of progression in Year 5

Working scientifically

Children will revisit the ideas and methods introduced in Years 3 and 4, including the concepts of comparative and fair tests. They will use a wider range of methods to record their results and data with increasing accuracy, including labelled scientific diagrams and models, as well as tables, bar graphs and line graphs. With support, they will distinguish between fact and opinion. They will continue to learn about how scientific ideas have developed over time, finding out about the work of influential scientists. Children will become more independent in designing their own enquiries and experiments and will outline the key variables when designing a fair test, considering how to effectively control them. They will also become more confident in using the results of their experiments to make predictions and suggest further research questions. They will report their findings orally and in writing, and learn how to use relevant scientific language and illustrations to communicate ideas. This continues in Year 6 as children become more independent scientific thinkers.

Living things and their habitats

Children will build on their Year 2 and 4 work, studying the life cycles of animals (mammals, amphibians, insects and birds) and plants in greater depth (focusing on birth, growth, development, reproduction and death in animals, and growth, reproduction and death in plants). They will make observations of plant and animal reproduction by growing plants, or rearing and caring for baby animals, and will work scientifically when they make observations of animal and plant life cycles in the local environment. They will extend this by finding out about the work of naturalists and animal behaviourists, making comparisons and beginning to think about possible reasons for similarities and differences.

Animals, including humans

Developing from their work on life cycles in Year 2, children will learn about changes in humans as they develop from birth to death. They will draw timelines to indicate stages in the growth and development of humans and learn about changes experienced in puberty.

Properties and changes of materials

This links with Year 3 and 4 work on magnetism and electricity and the states of matter. Children conduct tests to identify the properties of everyday materials (hardness, solubility, conductivity and magnetism) and experiment with different materials to find out about reversible changes (melting, dissolving and evaporating). They learn how to recover substances from solution, through evaporation, and explore ways of separating mixtures into solids and liquids by filtering and sieving. Children will experiment with heating, cooling, dissolving and mixing different substances to understand the concepts of reversible change and changes of state. This will enable them to draw connections to irreversible or hard to reverse changes (burning, rusting or other chemical reactions). With support, they will observe the effect of burning, or the irreversible chemical changes involved in cooking. Children will find out about scientists who helped to create new materials with advantageous properties through chemical change, and learn how these materials can be used.

Earth and space

Children will learn about the solar system and the way that the Earth moves relative to the Sun, and the Moon relative to the Earth. They will create and use simple models of the solar system and use these to demonstrate why we experience day and night on Earth. They will find out about different time zones and understand why it isn't the same time all over Earth simultaneously. They will also learn about how our heliocentric (Sun-centred) model of the solar system differs from the geocentric (Earth-centred) model used in the past.

Forces

Building on their Year 3 work on forces and magnets, children learn about the effects of gravity and drag forces, such as friction and air and water resistance. They will find out how and why drag forces slow moving objects down, devising experiments to show air resistance, or look at how friction works to slow down a wheeled vehicle when a brake is applied. Children will learn how levers, pulleys, gears and springs work, and how they transfer force and motion. They will look at the work of scientists such as Galileo and Isaac Newton.

Medium-term planning Autumn 1: Animals inc. humans

YEAR 5

W	Outcomes	Curriculum objectives	Working scientifically
1	• To begin to consider life cycles. • To know that human bodies vary naturally. • To know that humans have a growth spurt and that body parts change in proportion during growth. • To know about the changes that take place at puberty.	• To describe the changes as humans develop to old age.	• To record data and results of increasing complexity using scientific diagrams and labels, classification keys, tables, scatter graphs, bar and line graphs. • To identify scientific evidence that has been used to support or refute ideas or arguments.
2	• To know about the structure and function of the male and female reproductive systems. • To know about the development of the baby in the womb. • To understand the difference between a life cycle and a time line. • To know and recognise the stages in the human time line.	• To describe the changes as humans develop to old age.	• To report and present findings from enquiries in written forms such as in displays and other presentations. • To identify scientific evidence that has been used to support or refute ideas or arguments.
3	• To learn about the life cycles of mammals. • To research and present information about the three kinds of mammals. • To learn about the life cycle of a bird and a frog. • To find out about the risks to survival during the life cycle. • To learn about the different kinds of amphibians.	• To describe the changes as humans develop to old age. • (Y5 Living things and their habitats) To describe the differences in the life cycles of a mammal, an amphibian, an insect and a bird.	• To plan enquiries, including recognising and controlling variables where necessary. • To record data and results using scientific diagrams and labels, classification keys, tables, scatter graphs, bar and line graphs. • To present findings in oral and written forms such as displays and other presentations. • To identify scientific evidence that has been used to support or refute ideas or arguments.
4	• To learn about the life cycle of the butterfly and the eel. • To learn that some insects have nymph stages instead of caterpillar stages. • To research the life cycles of rainforest animals. • To relate items on the shore to life cycles of marine animals. • To research the life cycles of animal in different regions of the ocean.	• To describe the changes as humans develop to old age. • (Y5 Living things and their habitats) To describe the differences in the life cycles of a mammal, an amphibian, an insect and a bird.	• To plan enquiries, including recognising and controlling variables where necessary. • To identify scientific evidence that has been used to support or refute ideas.
5	• To research the life cycles of desert animals and dinosaurs. • To learn about the life of David Attenborough.	• To describe the changes as humans develop to old age.	• To record data using line graphs. • To present findings in oral and written forms such as displays and other presentations.
6	• To investigate camouflage patterns. • To learn about the life of Jane Goodall.	• To describe the changes as humans develop to old age.	• To plan enquiries including recognising and controlling variables. • To report findings from enquiries, including causal relationships and explanations. • To present findings in oral and written forms such as displays and other presentations.
Assess and review		• Revision and assessment of the half term's work.	

Medium-term planning Autumn 2: Properties of materials

W	Outcomes	Curriculum objectives	Working scientifically
1	• To identify the properties of solids, liquids and gases and provide examples. • To show how a simple electrical circuit is constructed. • To devise and carry out an investigation into the hardness of materials. • To devise and carry out an investigation into the electrical conductivity of materials.	• To compare and group together everyday materials on the basis of their properties, including their hardness, solubility, transparency, conductivity (electrical and thermal), and response to magnets.	• To plan enquiries, including recognising and controlling variables. • To present findings in written form.
2	• To devise and carry out an investigation into the thermal conductivity of materials. • To devise and carry out an investigation into the response to magnets of materials.	• To compare and group together everyday materials on the basis of their properties, including their hardness, solubility, transparency, conductivity (electrical and thermal), and response to magnets.	• To plan enquiries, including recognising and controlling variables. • To use test results to make predictions to set up further comparative and fair tests. • To present findings in written form.
3	• To link the properties of materials with their everyday uses. • To use research skills to find out more information. • To devise and carry out an investigation into the waterproof properties of fabrics.	• To give reasons, based on evidence from comparative and fair tests, for the particular uses of everyday materials.	• To report findings from enquiries, including conclusions, causal relationships and explanations of and degree of trust in results. • To plan enquiries, including recognising and controlling variables. • To take measurements with increasing accuracy and precision.
4	• To devise and carry out an investigation into the water absorbing properties of fabrics, bricks and rocks. • To link the properties of materials with their uses. • To learn about porous materials, and that soil has air in it.	• To use knowledge of solids, liquids and gases to decide how mixtures might be separated. • To give reasons, based on evidence from comparative and fair tests, for the particular uses of everyday materials.	• To use test results to make predictions to set up further comparative and fair tests. • To take measurements with increasing accuracy and precision. • To present findings in oral and written forms such as displays and other presentations.
5	• To understand how a sieve works. • To know how particles of different sizes can form different layers of sediment, and that this process can be used to separate materials. • To understand that when some mixtures mix with water some of their components may dissolve. • To identify substances which are soluble and insoluble in water.	• To compare and group together everyday materials on the basis of their properties, including their hardness, solubility, transparency, conductivity (electrical and thermal), and response to magnets. • To use knowledge of solids, liquids and gases to decide how mixtures might be separated. • To demonstrate that dissolving, mixing and changes of state are reversible changes.	• To plan enquiries, including recognising and controlling variables. • To record data using tables. • To report findings from enquiries, including conclusions, causal relationships and explanations of and degree of trust in results.
6	• To know that evaporation can be used as a means of recovering a dissolved solid. • To learn how mixing, dissolving, filtering and evaporation can be used in separating materials.	• To use knowledge of solids, liquids and gases to decide how mixtures might be separated. • To demonstrate that dissolving, mixing and changes of state are reversible changes.	• To report and present findings from enquiries.
Assess and review		• Revision and assessment of the half term's work.	

Medium-term planning Spring 1: Earth and space

W	Outcomes	Curriculum objectives	Working scientifically
1	• To study evidence for a spherical Earth. • To compare the sizes of Earth, Moon and Sun. • To understand that the Earth rotates and relate the Earth's rotation to the measurement of time. • To investigate the movement of the Sun across the sky.	• To describe the Sun, Earth and Moon as approximately spherical bodies. • To use the idea of the Earth's rotation to explain day and night.	• To take measurements with increasing accuracy and precision. • To record data in bar and line graphs. • To identify scientific evidence that has been used to support or refute ideas or arguments.
2	• To locate the different time zones. • To understand that the axis of the Earth tilts. • To know how the Earth moves around the Sun. • To relate the change in sunrise times to the angle of tilt, and the Earth's position on its orbit to the seasons.	• To describe the movement of the Earth relative to the Sun in the solar system. • To use the idea of the Earth's rotation to explain day and night.	• To record data using a line graph. • To report findings from enquiries, including conclusions, causal relationships and explanations.
3	• To relate the activities of living things and the weather to the angle of tilt, and the Earth's position on its orbit to the seasons. • To discover how the phases of the Moon occur. • To understand that as the Earth moves around the Sun, the Moon also moves around the Earth.	• To describe the movement of the Earth relative to the Sun in the solar system. • To describe the movement of the Moon relative to the Earth.	• To report findings from enquiries, including conclusions, causal relationships and explanations.
4	• To know the positions of the planets and the asteroid belt in the solar system. • To understand how moons are believed to have formed and to know the planets that have them. • To understand that there are different kinds of stars. • To understand the arrangement of stars in constellations.	• To describe the movement of the Earth relative to the Sun in the solar system.	• To plan different types of scientific enquiries. • To use a range of scientific equipment, with increasing accuracy and precision.
5	• To understand how scientists look for planets around stars. • To understand that the Sun is a star in a galaxy. • To understand the relationship of galaxies to the universe. • To understand the idea of the geocentric solar system and that the idea had flaws. • To study the life and work of Copernicus and Galileo.	• To describe the movement of the Earth relative to the Sun in the solar system.	• To identify scientific evidence that has been used to support or refute ideas or arguments.
6	• To understand that scientists use the work of others as the basis for their own work.	• To describe the movement of the Earth relative to the Sun in the solar system.	• To identify scientific evidence that has been used to support or refute ideas or arguments.
Assess and review		• Revision and assessment of the half term's work.	

Medium-term planning Spring 2: Living things

W	Outcomes	Curriculum objectives	Working scientifically
1	• To ascertain the accumulated knowledge of plants. • To investigate the processes that take place in germination. • To investigate the structure of single and composite flowers.	• To describe the life process of reproduction in some plants.	• To plan enquiries, including recognising and controlling variables where necessary. • To record data using scientific diagrams and classification keys. • To report and present findings from enquiries, including conclusions, causal relationships and explanations of and degree of trust in results, in oral and written forms such as displays and other presentations.
2	• To identify the pollen producing and pollen receiving parts of the flower. • To identify pollinating insects. • To identify wind pollinated plants and importance of wind pollination to cereal crops. • To explore the diversity of seed dispersal. • To discuss the ways in which seeds are dispersed.	• To describe the life process of reproduction in some plants.	• To report and present findings from enquiries, including conclusions, causal relationships and explanations of and degree of trust in results, in oral and written forms such as displays and other presentations.
3	• To distinguish between ephemerals, annuals, biennials, herbaceous perennials and woody perennials. • To describe in detail the plants in a habitat using botanical vocabulary. • To explore how plants have adapted to life in a rainforest.	• To describe the life process of reproduction in some plants.	• To record data and results using scientific diagrams and labels, classification keys, tables, bar and line graphs, and models. • To present findings in oral and written forms such as displays and other presentations.
4	• To explore how seaweeds are adapted for shore life. • To learn about how plant life cycles are adapted for desert conditions. • To investigate how stems absorb water from the ground. • To study prehistoric plants. • To investigate a 'living fossil'.	• To describe the life process of reproduction in some plants.	• To plan enquiries, including recognising and controlling variables. • To record data and results using scientific diagrams and labels, classification keys, tables, bar and line graphs, and models. • To report findings from enquiries, including oral and written explanations of results, explanations involving causal relationships and conclusions.
5	• To learn about Theophrastus, John Ray and Joseph Banks and their work on plants. • To learn about Kew Gardens.	• To describe the life process of reproduction in some plants.	• To identify scientific evidence that has been used to support or refute ideas or arguments.
6	• To use a knowledge of plants to set up a garden, flower bed or vegetable plot.	• To describe the life process of reproduction in some plants.	• To plan enquiries, including recognising and controlling variables where necessary.
Assess and review		• Revision and assessment of the half term's work.	

Medium-term planning Summer 1: Properties of materials

W	Outcomes	Curriculum objectives	Working scientifically
1	• To identify a range of reversible changes. • To introduce the concept that some changes form new materials. • To discover how invisible ink works and investigate suitable materials for invisible inks. • To observe changes that take place when water and plaster of Paris are mixed.	• To explain that some changes result in the formation of new materials, and that this kind of change is not usually reversible.	• To plan enquiries including recognising and controlling variables where necessary. • To present findings in oral and written forms such as displays and other presentations. • To identify scientific evidence that has been used to support or refute ideas or arguments.
2	• To investigate the effect of heat on foods. • To compare the effect of heat on dough. • To investigate properties of biscuits made in different proportions of ingredients and different baking times.	• To explain that some changes result in the formation of new materials, and that this kind of change is not usually reversible, including changes associated with burning.	• To plan enquiries including recognising and controlling variables where necessary. • To record data and results using tables. • To present findings in displays and other presentations.
3	• To consider the effect of burning on a range of materials. • To consider the changes that take place when a candle burns. • To know the changes that take place when vinegar is added to bicarbonate. • To know the effect of the gas produced on a flame. • To understand the science behind the techniques of fighting fires.	• To explain that some changes result in the formation of new materials, and that this kind of change is not usually reversible, including changes associated with burning and the action of acid on bicarbonate of soda.	• To plan enquiries including recognising and controlling variables where necessary. • To take measurements, using a range of scientific equipment, with increasing accuracy and precision. • To record results in a scientific diagram. • To present findings in displays and other presentations.
4	• To know that sometimes a gas is produced by an irreversible reaction. • To know the effect of diluting the vinegar on its reaction with bicarbonate of soda. • To learn about the processes taking place in a volcanic eruption.	• To explain that some changes result in the formation of new materials, and that this kind of change is not usually reversible, including changes associated with the action of acid on bicarbonate of soda.	• To record data and results using scientific diagrams. • To use test results to make predictions to set up further comparative and fair tests. • To present findings in oral and written forms such as displays and other presentations.
5	• To learn where rusting takes place and consider the factors that may cause rusting. • To know how to prevent rusting. • To understand the processes and work involved in using iron beneficially.	• To explain that some changes result in the formation of new materials, and that this kind of change is not usually reversible.	• To plan enquiries including recognising and controlling variables where necessary. • To present findings in oral and written forms such as displays and other presentations.
6	• To learn how polymers are created. • To understand the effect of temperature on the initial reaction. • To investigate the properties of plastics and compare them to other materials. • To find out about the life and work of a scientist and the impact of their discoveries.	• To explain that some changes result in the formation of new materials, and that this kind of change is not usually reversible.	• To plan enquiries including recognising and controlling variables where necessary. • To present findings in oral and written forms such as displays and other presentations.
Assess and review	• Revision and assessment of the half term's work.		

Medium-term planning Summer 2: Forces

W	Outcomes	Curriculum objectives	Working scientifically
1	• To revise how magnets attract some but not all metals. • To investigate magnetic forces acting at a distance. • To identify forces and their direction. • To know that the force that pulls an object down is its weight in Newtons.	• To explain that unsupported objects fall towards the Earth because of the force of gravity acting between the Earth and the falling object.	• To take measurements using a range of scientific equipment.
2	• To use research skills to find out how a scientist developed ideas. • To know that gravity isn't just an Earth phenomenon. • To compare the work of Galileo and Newton.	• To explain that unsupported objects fall towards the Earth because of the force of gravity acting between the Earth and the falling object.	• To plan enquires including recognising and controlling variables where necessary. • To record data and results of increasing complexity using scientific diagrams and labels, classification keys, tables, bar and line graphs. • To identify scientific evidence that has been used to support or refute ideas or arguments.
3	• To know that air produces a force that opposes motion. • To know that parachutes slow down the speed that an object falls. • To know that the size of a parachute changes how quickly an object falls. • To understand the differences between the resistance to motion of air and water.	• To identify the effects of air resistance, water resistance and friction, that act between moving surfaces.	• To plan enquiries including recognising and controlling variables where necessary. • To record data and results of increasing complexity using scientific diagrams and labels, classification keys, tables, bar and line graphs.
4	• To know that friction slows down movement. • To know that a Newton meter can be used to measure friction forces.	• To identify the effects of air resistance, water resistance and friction, that act between moving surfaces.	• To plan enquiries including recognising and controlling variables where necessary. • To record data and results of increasing complexity using scientific diagrams and labels, classification keys, tables, bar and line graphs. • To use test results to make predictions to set up further comparative and fair tests.
5	• To know that drag forces will stop an object unless a force is used to push it forward. • To know that brakes must have high friction to make them effective. • To know how speed and other factors affect how quickly a car can stop.	• To identify the effects of air resistance, water resistance and friction, that act between moving surfaces.	• To use test results to make predictions to set up further comparative and fair tests.
6	• To know some simple machines that are used to assist movement. • To know how some simple machines and how the length of a lever can make moving a load easier.	• To recognise that some mechanisms, including levers, pulleys and gears, allow a smaller force to have a greater effect.	• To use test results to make predictions to set up further comparative and fair tests.
Assess and review		• Revision and assessment of the half term's work.	

Background knowledge

Children will have the opportunity to consolidate their understanding of the scientific ideas and methods introduced in previous years (i.e. the concept of a fair test). Their observations and measurements will be increasingly accurate, and they will become more skilled and independent in analysing data. They will be able to use the results of their experiments to design new enquiries and predict possible outcomes. Children will be expected to take more responsibility for the planning of investigations, including considering which variable to change and which to control, and be able to justify their choices. They will need to begin to focus on the differences between fact and opinion in a scientific context, and look at how scientific ideas have developed and changed over time.

Fact and opinion

Most children will be familiar with the concepts of fact and opinion and how these differ, both from their work in literacy and also from everyday experience. At this stage, they can begin applying these concepts to their scientific thinking. This is helpful because it encourages children to think more rigorously about the quality of scientific evidence. They can be encouraged to think about how we know that a particular statement, for example 'pulse and breathing rate increase when you exercise,' is a fact rather than an opinion. They will begin to see that experimental data, when analysed correctly, can help to prove a particular assertion or idea as fact. They may know from their own experience that they get out of breath when running, but in order to prove that a high breathing rate is directly linked to exercise they would need to construct a fair test to find out if this happens to everyone.

Understanding how scientific ideas develop over time

Thinking about fact and opinion is helpful in the context of learning about how scientific ideas have developed over time. Children will need to understand that science is an ongoing process – scientists build on work done by people in the past in order to understand the world more fully. Some concepts are difficult to prove as fact, and so theories are developed based on what is known or can be tested. Scientists of the future will develop the work being done now, and no doubt some ideas we believe are true will be proven false or only partly accurate. Children will think about this when they learn about the geocentric model of the solar system and understand how, for centuries, people believed that the Earth was at the centre of the universe. It wasn't until the work of Nicolaus Copernicus in the 16th century that the heliocentric model of the solar system began to be accepted. Children will need to understand that before the 16th century, scientists believed the geocentric model to be true because it seemed to explain some of the phenomena they observed (for example, the way that gravity causes objects to fall towards the Earth). As time went on, scientists noticed discrepancies that couldn't be explained by this model, so they had to alter their theories.

Vocabulary and concepts to introduce in Year 5

Living things and their habitats and Animals, including humans (as for previous years, plus): *anther, asexual reproduction animal behaviourist, birth, bud, carpel, chromosomes, cross-pollination, death, egg cell (ovum), embryo, fallopian tubes, female gamete, fertilization, filament, gestation, growth, hormones, life cycles, male gamete, menstrual cycle, microorganisms, naturalist, ovaries, ovary, ovulation, penis, petals, placenta, puberty, sepals, sexual reproduction, sperm, stamens, stigma, style, testes, uterus, vagina, vertebrates (reptiles, fish, amphibians, birds, mammals), zygote*

Properties and changes of materials: *buoyancy, burning, change of state, chemical changes, chemical reaction, density, dissolving, elasticity, electrical conductivity, evaporating, filtering, filtrate, gas, hardness, irreversible or hard-to-reverse change, liquid, melting, magnetism, polymer, residue, reversible change, rusting (oxidisation), sieving, solid, solubility, solute, solution, solvent, stiffness, strength, suspension, thermal conductivity, toughness*

Earth and space: *asteroids, axis, celestial body, comets, Earth, Earth's rotation, elliptical orbit, gravitational force, heliocentric model of the solar system, galaxy, geocentric model, hemisphere, Jupiter, light year, Mars, Mercury, meteors, moon, Neptune, phases of the moon, Saturn, shadow clock, shooting stars, Sun, sundial, time zones, Uranus, Venus*

Forces (as for Year 3, plus): *drag forces, gears, levers, pulleys, springs, transference of force and motion*

■SCHOLASTIC

Year 6 Long-term planning

Working scientifically

- Children in Years 5 and 6 should use their science experiences to: explore ideas and raise different kinds of questions; select and plan the most appropriate type of scientific enquiry to use to answer scientific questions; recognise when and how to set up comparative and fair tests and explain which variables need to be controlled and why. They should use and develop keys and other information records to identify, classify and describe living things and materials, and identify patterns that might be found in the natural environment. They should make their own decisions about what observations to make, what measurements to use and how long to make them for, and whether to repeat them; choose the most appropriate equipment to make measurements and explain how to use it accurately. They should decide how to record data from a choice of familiar approaches; look for different causal relationships in their data and identify evidence that refutes or supports their ideas. They should use their results to identify when further tests and observations might be needed; recognise which secondary sources will be most useful to research their ideas and begin to separate opinion from fact. They should use relevant scientific language and illustrations to discuss, communicate and justify their scientific ideas and should talk about how scientific ideas have developed over time.
- These opportunities for working scientifically should be provided across Years 5 and 6 so that the expectations in the programme of study can be met by the end of Year 6. Pupils are not expected to cover each aspect for every area of study.

Living things and their habitats

- Children should build on their learning about grouping living things in Year 4 by looking at the classification system in more detail. They should be introduced to the idea that broad groupings, such as micro-organisms, plants and animals can be subdivided. Through direct observations where possible, they should classify animals into commonly found invertebrates and vertebrates. They should discuss reasons why living things are placed in one group and not another.
- Children might find out about the significance of the work of scientists such as Carl Linnaeus.
- Children might work scientifically by: using classification systems and keys to identify some animals and plants in the immediate environment. They could research unfamiliar animals and plants from a broad range of other habitats and decide where they belong in the classification system.

Animals, including humans

- Children should build on their learning from Years 3 and 4 about the main body parts and internal organs to explore and answer questions that help them to understand how the circulatory system enables the body to function.
- Children should learn how to keep their bodies healthy and how their bodies might be damaged.
- Children might work scientifically by: exploring the work of scientists and scientific research about the relationship between diet, exercise, drugs, lifestyle and health.

Evolution and inheritance

- Building on what they learned about fossils in the topic on rocks in Year 3, children should find out more about how living things on Earth have changed over time. They should be introduced to the idea that characteristics are passed from parents to their offspring, for instance by considering different breeds of dogs, and what happens when, for example, labradors are crossed with poodles. They should also appreciate that variation in offspring over time can make animals more or less able to survive in particular environments, for example, by exploring how giraffes' necks got longer, or the development of insulating fur on the arctic fox. Children might find out about the work of palaeontologists such as Mary Anning and about how Charles Darwin and Alfred Wallace developed their ideas on evolution.
- **Note**: At this stage, children are not expected to understand how genes and chromosomes work.
- Children might work scientifically by: observing and raising questions about local animals and how they are adapted to their environment; comparing how some living things are adapted to survive in extreme conditions, for example, cactuses, penguins and camels. They might analyse the advantages and disadvantages of specific adaptations, such as being on two feet rather than four, having a long or a short beak, having gills or lungs, tendrils on climbing plants, brightly coloured and scented flowers.

Light

- Children should build on the work on light in Year 3, exploring the way that light behaves, including light sources, reflection and shadows. They should talk about what happens and make predictions.
- Children might work scientifically by: deciding where to place rear-view mirrors on cars; designing and making a periscope and using the idea that light appears to travel in straight lines to explain how it works. They might investigate the relationship between light sources, objects and shadows by using shadow puppets. They could extend their experience of light by looking at a range of phenomena including rainbows, colours on soap bubbles, objects looking bent in water and coloured filters (they do not need to explain why these phenomena occur).

Electricity

- Building on their work in Year 4, children should construct simple series circuits, to help them to answer questions about what happens when they try different components, for example, switches, bulbs, buzzers and motors. They should learn how to represent a simple circuit in a diagram using recognised symbols.
- **Note**: Children are expected to learn only about series circuits, not parallel circuits. Children should be taught to take the necessary precautions for working safely with electricity.
- Children might work scientifically by: systematically identifying the effect of changing one component at a time in a circuit; designing and making a set of traffic lights, a burglar alarm or some other useful circuit.

Overview of progression in Year 6

Working scientifically

Building on the concepts, ideas and methods in Year 5, children will have opportunities to become still more independent in devising fair and comparative tests and experiments, controlling variables and thinking about how to make sure their results are reliable. They will use a range of scientific and everyday equipment to take accurate measurements, and learn how to record and explain their data clearly using a range of formats (introduced in Year 5). They will learn how to use and create their own classification keys when grouping plants and animals. Children will be learning to think critically and evaluate the evidence they get from their own tests and experiments, and from research using secondary sources. They will explain their results and findings in terms of causal relationships (i.e. focusing on likely reasons for the phenomena they observe, and the links between cause and effect). They will also begin to be more confident in identifying the specific scientific evidence that is used to support a particular idea or argument. They will be able to make links between different areas of their learning, and get to grips with more abstract concepts.

Living things and their habitats

Extending the work in Year 4 on classification, children learn about classifying living things into five 'kingdoms' and animals into vertebrates (reptiles, fish, amphibians, birds and mammals) and invertebrates, using direct observation and explaining their choices. They use classification keys to help with (and to demonstrate) the decision-making process involved.

Animals, including humans

Building on their work in Years 3 and 4 on human digestion, circulation, muscles and skeleton, children will learn about the human circulatory system (identifying the functions of the heart, blood vessels and blood) and look at how diet, exercise, drugs and lifestyle impact on health. They will compare and contrast the needs of different animals (including humans), and find out about how nutrients and water are transported within our (and animals') bodies. They work scientifically to make drawings and models to show ideas about the circulatory system, and compare these with images from secondary sources. They may also conduct experiments and tests to show the effect of different activities on pulse and breathing rate, suggesting reasons for their findings. They will have an opportunity to learn about scientists whose work has contributed to our understanding of the circulatory system, including Harvey and Galen.

Evolution and inheritance

Children will be introduced to the idea that characteristics are passed from parent to child, in plants and animals, including humans. They build on their fossil work from Year 3, and look at how plants and animals on Earth adapt to their environment, gradually change over time, and how living things evolve. They learn that offspring are not identical to their parents, and that this variation can give rise to characteristics that help or hinder animals' chances of survival, leading over long periods of time to evolutionary change. Children may also start to learn about Charles Darwin's work and its contribution to our understanding of evolution.

Light

Extending their work in Year 3, children do practical experiments and make observations of the way light travels, looking at different effects of light in phenomena such as rainbows, rays of light split by prisms, objects appearing bent in water, etc. They look at how light appears to travel in straight lines, and understand that we can see objects because they reflect light into our eyes. They know that shadows are the same shape as the object that cast them and experiment with shadows by placing objects at different distances from a light source.

Electricity

To develop their work from Year 4, children construct simple electrical series circuits using a range of components (switches, buzzers, motors etc). They can name the parts of a circuit and draw diagrams using recognised symbols. They experiment by adding cells to a circuit, or using cells with a higher voltage, to make a lamp shine brighter, or a buzzer buzz louder.

Medium-term planning Autumn 1: Living things

W	Outcomes	Curriculum objectives	Working scientifically
1	• To introduce the idea of a more detailed classification system. • To know how to place organisms into one of the five kingdoms. • To learn about the development of microscopes and research of cells.	• To describe how living things are classified into broad groups according to common observable characteristics and based on similarities and differences, including micro-organisms, plants and animals.	• To record data and results using classification keys. • To identify scientific evidence that has been used to support or refute ideas or arguments.
2	• To learn about bacteria. • To understand the role of protists in food webs. • To learn about yeast.	• To describe how living things are classified into broad groups according to common observable characteristics and based on similarities and differences, including micro-organisms, plants and animals.	• To plan enquiries, including recognising and controlling variables where necessary. • To take measurements, using a range of scientific equipment, with increasing accuracy and precision. • To record data and results using classification keys.
3	• To learn about responses in controlling the spread of a virus. • To be able to classify vertebrates and invertebrates based upon their characteristics.	• To describe how living things are classified into broad groups according to common observable characteristics and based on similarities and differences, including micro-organisms, plants and animals.	• To record data and results using classification keys.
Assess and review	• Revision and assessment of the half term's work.		

Medium-term planning Autumn 1: Evolution and inheritance

W	Outcomes	Curriculum objectives	Working scientifically
4	• To review ideas about fossil formation and adaptation to habitats. • To consider issues of difference between people with sensitivity. • To find out about the life and work of Mary Anning.	• To recognise that living things have changed over time and that fossils provide information about living things that inhabited the Earth millions of years ago. • To recognise that living things produce offspring of the same kind, but normally offspring vary and are not identical to their parents.	• To plan different types of scientific enquiries to answer questions. • To report and present findings from enquiries. • To identify scientific evidence.
5	• To recognise a fossil and know that fossils can provide evidence of soft remains and of footprints. • To consider why humans walk on two legs. • To understand that changes in the environment can cause some groups of living things to become extinct.	• To recognise that living things have changed over time and that fossils provide information about living things that inhabited the Earth millions of years ago. • To identify how animals and plants are adapted to suit their environment in different ways.	• To plan different types of scientific enquiries to answer questions. • To report and present findings from enquiries, including conclusions,
6	• To consider how animals have adapted to their environment. • To understand that animals are in competition for resources. • To use results of games that model competition to make inferences about competition in the wild.	• To identify how animals and plants are adapted to suit their environment in different ways.	• To use test results to make predictions to set up further comparative and fair tests. • To report and present findings from enquiries.
Assess and review	• Revision and assessment of the half term's work.		

Medium-term planning Autumn 2: Animals, inc. humans

W	Outcomes	Curriculum objectives	Working scientifically
1	• To recall the components of a healthy diet. • To demonstrate knowledge and understanding of the digestive system. • To recognise the organisation and extent of the circulatory system in the human body. • To know that the pulse is produced by the heart beat.	• To identify and name the main parts of the human circulatory system, and describe the functions of the heart, blood vessels and blood.	• To plan enquiries, including recognising and controlling variables where necessary. • To take measurements with increasing accuracy and precision. • To report findings from enquiries, including explanations of results in oral and written forms.
2	• To know that the pulse rate varies with activity. • To identify the parts of the heart. • To understand how the heart works. • To know the pulse can be used to assess fitness.	• To identify and name the main parts of the human circulatory system, and describe the functions of the heart, blood vessels and blood.	• To plan enquiries, including recognising and controlling variables where necessary. • To take measurements with increasing accuracy and precision. • To record data and results of increasing complexity using scientific diagrams and labels, classification keys, tables, bar and line graphs.
3	• To know that organs work together. • To know the positions and functions of the major organs of the body. • To understand Galen's ideas about the circulation of the blood. • To understand how Harvey showed that Galen's ideas about circulation were wrong.	• To identify and name the main parts of the human circulatory system, and describe the functions of the heart, blood vessels and blood.	• To take measurements with increasing accuracy and precision. • To record data and results using tables and line graphs. • To report findings from enquiries, including conclusions, causal relationships and explanations. • To identify scientific evidence that has been used to support or refute ideas or arguments.
4	• To distinguish between arteries, veins and capillaries. • To understand the links between the circulatory system and the major organs. • To identify the components of the blood. • To learn about how a clot forms and the function of white blood cells. • To examine the structure of the respiratory system. • To record the breathing rate.	• To identify and name the main parts of the human circulatory system, and describe the functions of the heart, blood vessels and blood.	• To record data and results of increasing complexity using scientific diagrams and labels, classification keys, tables, bar and line graphs. • To present findings in written forms such as displays and other presentations.
5	• To investigate pulse rates, breathing rates and activity. • To review the functions of the heart and lungs. • To link diet, exercise and hygiene to general health.	• To identify and name the main parts of the human circulatory system, and describe the functions of the heart, blood vessels and blood.	• To present findings in written forms such as displays and other presentations.
6	• To examine factors which can damage the body organs. • To compare organ systems in a range of vertebrates. • To find out about the organ systems in invertebrates.	• To identify and name the main parts of the human circulatory system, and describe the functions of the heart, blood vessels and blood.	• To present findings in written forms such as displays and other presentations.
Assess and review		• Revision and assessment of the half term's work.	

Medium-term planning Spring 1: Light

W	Outcomes	Curriculum objectives	Working scientifically
1	• To understand the differences between the meaning of transparent, translucent and opaque. • To identify that light travels in a straight line. • To know light travels from a light source.	• To recognise that light appears to travel in straight lines. • To use the idea that light travels in straight lines to explain that objects are seen because they give out or reflect light into the eye.	• To present findings in oral and written forms such as displays and other presentations.
2	• To know that light must be reflected from non-luminous objects in order for them to be seen. • To understand how the eye detects light. • To investigate how eye position tells us whether an animal is hunted or a hunter.	• To use the idea that light travels in straight lines to explain that objects are seen because they give out or reflect light into the eye. • To explain that we see things because light travels from light sources to our eyes or from light sources to objects and then to our eyes.	• To report findings from enquiries, including conclusions, causal relationships and explanations, in oral and written forms. • To identify scientific evidence that has been used to support or refute ideas or arguments.
3	• To know that mirrors change the direction of light. • To know that the direction that the light is reflected can be predicted. • To know how mirrors can be used to see in places that cannot be seen directly.	• To use the idea that light travels in straight lines to explain that objects are seen because they give out or reflect light into the eye.	• To take measurements, using a range of scientific equipment, with increasing accuracy and precision. • To report findings from enquiries, including conclusions, causal relationships and explanations, in oral and written forms.
4	• To know that Newton worked on ideas other than forces. • To know how Newton separated white light. • To know the effects of white light being separated.	• To use the idea that light travels in straight lines to explain that objects are seen because they give out or reflect light into the eye.	• To report findings from enquiries, including conclusions, causal relationships and explanations, in oral and written forms. • To identify scientific evidence that has been used to support or refute ideas or arguments.
5	• To understand and explain that the shape of the face directed at a light source causes a shadow. • To know that 2D shapes produce more predictable shadows. • To know that the size of the shadow depends on several factors.	• To use the idea that light travels in straight lines to explain why shadows have the same shape as the objects that cast them.	• To take measurements, using a range of scientific equipment, with increasing accuracy and precision. • To present findings in oral and written forms such as displays and other presentations.
6	• To know that shadow size depends on the angle of light. • To understand how the direction of the light source influences the way objects appear in terms of reflection and regions of shadow. • To know that when light travels through different materials it can change direction.	• To use the idea that light travels in straight lines to explain why shadows have the same shape as the objects that cast them.	• To record data and results of increasing complexity using scientific diagrams and labels, classification keys, tables and bar and line graphs. • To present findings in oral and written forms such as displays and other presentations.
Assess and review		• Revision and assessment of the half term's work.	

Medium-term planning Spring 2: Electricity

W	Outcomes	Curriculum objectives	Working scientifically
1	• To know that electricity can be controlled to do different jobs. • To know how to light a bulb in an electrical circuit. • To name the parts of a circuit. • To know how to build a simple circuit that makes a bulb light or a buzzer sound.	• To compare and give reasons for variations in how components function, including the brightness of bulbs, the loudness of buzzers and the on/off position of switches.	• To take measurements, using a range of scientific equipment. • To use test results to make predictions to set up further comparative tests. • To present findings in displays and other presentations.
2	• To understand how switches can control the flow of electricity around a circuit. • To know that the number of bulbs and batteries in a circuit will affect how bright the bulbs are.	• To associate the brightness of a lamp or the volume of a buzzer with the number and voltage of cells used in the circuit.	• To plan enquiries, including recognising and controlling variables where necessary. • To report and present findings from enquiries, including conclusions, causal relationships and explanations, in oral and written forms such as displays and other presentations.
3	• To learn why Faraday is famous.	• To compare and give reasons for variations in how components function, including the brightness of bulbs, the loudness of buzzers and the on/off position of switches.	• To take measurements, using a range of scientific equipment. • To report and present findings from enquiries, including conclusions, causal relationships and explanations, in oral and written forms such as displays and other presentations.
4	• To consider the path of electricity in different circuit designs. • To know that the more wire in the circuit, the dimmer the bulb. • To understand how very long telephone wires might affect the quality of the signal.	• To compare and give reasons for variations in how components function, including the brightness of bulbs, the loudness of buzzers and the on/off position of switches. • To use recognised symbols when representing a simple circuit in a diagram.	• To take measurements, using a range of scientific equipment, with increasing accuracy and precision. • To report and present findings from enquiries, including conclusions, causal relationships and explanations, in oral and written forms such as displays and other presentations.
5	• To know how the position of a switch or switches will make a circuit change how it works. • To understand how lights in different rooms can be on and off at different times. • To know that batteries provide a portable supply of electricity, but mains electricity produces more power.	• To compare and give reasons for variations in how components function, including the brightness of bulbs, the loudness of buzzers and the on/off position of switches.	• To report and present findings from enquiries, including conclusions, causal relationships and explanations, in oral and written forms such as displays and other presentations.
6	• To know that care is needed whenever using electricity. • To know that electricity is important to everyday life. • To describe a number of ways of generating electricity.	• To associate the brightness of a lamp or the volume of a buzzer with the number and voltage of cells used in the circuit. • To compare and give reasons for variations in how components function, including the brightness of bulbs, the loudness of buzzers and the on/off position of switches. • To use recognised symbols when representing a simple circuit in a diagram.	• To report and present findings from enquiries, including conclusions, causal relationships and explanations of and degree of trust in results, in oral and written forms such as displays and other presentations.
Assess and review		• Revision and assessment of the half term's work.	

Medium-term planning Summer 1: Evolution and inheritance

W	Outcomes	Curriculum objectives	Working scientifically
1	• To review the idea that characteristics are passed from parents to offspring. • To be able to define what is meant by the term species. • To be able to explain causes of variation. • To be able to classify variations as continuous or discontinuous.	• To recognise that living things produce offspring of the same kind, but normally offspring vary and are not identical to their parents.	• To record data and results of increasing complexity using scientific diagrams and labels, classification keys, tables, bar and line graphs.
2	• To understand that special designs which help an animal to survive in its habitat are called adaptations. • To be able to give examples of how living things are adapted to survive in extreme environments. • To recognise adaptations of predators. • To explore strategies used by prey to avoid capture.	• To identify how animals and plants are adapted to suit their environment in different ways and that adaptation may lead to evolution.	• To plan enquiries, including recognising and controlling variables where necessary. • To take measurements, using a range of scientific equipment, with increasing accuracy and precision. • To report findings from enquiries, including conclusions, causal relationships and explanations of results, in oral and written forms.
3	• To appreciate that adaptation can lead to highly specialised designs. • To be able to give examples of the evidence Darwin used to support his theory of evolution. • To be able to identify evidence supporting Darwin's theory of evolution.	• To identify how animals and plants are adapted to suit their environment in different ways and that adaptation may lead to evolution.	• To plan enquiries, including recognising and controlling variables where necessary. • To take measurements, using a range of scientific equipment, with increasing accuracy and precision.
4	• To be able to describe examples of natural selection in action. • To explore how the behaviour of organisms can improve their chance of survival.	• To identify how animals and plants are adapted to suit their environment in different ways and that adaptation may lead to evolution.	• To plan enquiries, including recognising and controlling variables where necessary. • To present findings in oral and written forms such as displays and other presentations.
5	• To understand that competition favours the best adapted for survival. • To look at leaves of native vs introduced species – compare number of marks. • To understand how living things in the same habitat can avoid competition. • To appreciate that modern humans are just one survivor of a number of hominid ancestors.	• To identify how animals and plants are adapted to suit their environment in different ways and that adaptation may lead to evolution.	• To take measurements, using a range of scientific equipment, with increasing accuracy and precision. • To present findings in oral and written forms such as displays and other presentations.
6	• To learn about the work of behavioural scientists. • To investigate the impact of new technology on established scientific ideas.	• To recognise that living things have changed over time.	• To identify scientific evidence that has been used to support or refute ideas or arguments.
Assess and review	• Revision and assessment of the half term's work.		

Medium-term planning Summer 2: Animals, inc. humans

W	Outcomes	Curriculum objectives	Working scientifically
1	• To review understanding of digestion. • To appreciate and be able to explain why we need food. • To recognise the importance of a healthy diet. • To know the major food groups. • To be able to explain what a balanced diet is and why it is important. • To explore the ingredients used in a range of familiar meals and assess the nutritional value.	• To recognise the impact of diet, exercise, drugs and lifestyle on the way their bodies function.	• To plan different types of scientific enquiries to answer questions, including recognising and controlling variables where necessary. • To take measurements, using a range of scientific equipment, with increasing accuracy and precision. • To report and present findings from enquiries, including conclusions, causal relationships and explanations of results, in oral and written forms such as displays and other presentations.
2	• To plan and produce meals of high nutritional value. • To be able to explain why exercise is important for our health. • To be able to identify the different types of exercise needed to maintain health and develop fitness.	• To recognise the impact of diet, exercise, drugs and lifestyle on the way their bodies function.	• To record data and results of increasing complexity using scientific diagrams and labels, classification keys, tables, and bar and line graphs. • To use test results to make predictions to set up further comparative and fair tests. • To report and present findings from enquiries, including conclusions, causal relationships and explanations of results, in oral and written forms such as displays and other presentations. • To identify scientific evidence that has been used to support or refute ideas or arguments.
3	• To be aware of the benefits of healthy routines in their daily lives and common risks which they should avoid. • To understand why some lifestyle choices may be harmful to our health. • To know how to plan a regime for a healthy life.	• To recognise the impact of diet, exercise, drugs and lifestyle on the way their bodies function.	• To plan different types of scientific enquiries to answer questions, including recognising and controlling variables where necessary. • To use test results to make predictions to set up further comparative and fair tests. • To report and present findings from enquiries, including conclusions, causal relationships and explanations of results, in oral and written forms such as displays and other presentations. • To identify scientific evidence that has been used to support or refute ideas or arguments.
Assess and review		• Revision and assessment of the half term's work.	

Background knowledge

Year 6 gives children further opportunities to consolidate their understanding of the scientific concepts and methods introduced in Key Stage 2, making links between the areas of their learning to take a 'bigger picture' view of interrelationships, systems and processes. By Year 6, children will be able to draw on their existing knowledge to process more abstract ideas, and begin to appreciate the wider implications of scientific concepts outside their immediate experience. During this year they will also refine the way they report their findings from experiments and tests they have undertaken – in both oral and written reports they will need to understand how to create clear explanations involving causal relationships. They will also build on the work done on fact and opinion in Year 5 in order to identify the specific scientific evidence that has been used to support a particular theory or idea, explaining it in their own words or using simple models.

Explanations involving causal relationships

In Year 6, children will be building on their previous work on data analysis. When explaining the results of an experiment or reporting their research into a topic, they will need to begin to draw out the causal relationships. It's not always enough to show that a particular phenomenon has occurred – children will also need to show an understanding of why this has happened, what caused it and what it means. There are plenty of opportunities for this kind of approach in the programme of study for Year 6. For example, in 'Forces', children will look at how motion can be transferred using mechanical devices like pulleys and levers. They could draw diagrams or make models that show how a lever allows a small movement (pressing down on the 'handle' end of the lever) to be transferred into a much more powerful movement at the other end of the lever. In 'Evolution and inheritance', children's explanations will need to include the causal relationship between the small-scale adaptations that happen on an individual level as offspring differ from their parents, and the evolutionary change that can eventually result from this.

How scientific evidence can support or refute an idea

When children are familiar with the idea that scientific ideas develop over time, and with the differences between fact and opinion in a scientific context, they will be able to understand more clearly how scientific evidence can be used to support or refute a particular idea. This is an important concept for all of us to understand, whether we go on to develop a scientific career or not. Children can begin to learn to make, and justify, their own judgements about whether a piece of evidence put forward in support of an argument is valid or not. This skill will help them in later life too, when they want to work out whether a particular argument or theory they hear about in the media is scientifically plausible or not.

Vocabulary and concepts to introduce in Year 6

Living things and their habitats (as for previous years, plus): *classification, classification keys, dichotomous/binary keys, five kingdoms (bacteria, protists, animals, plants, fungi), genetic variation, invertebrates, vertebrates (reptiles, fish, amphibians, birds, mammals)*

Animals, including humans (as for previous years plus): *adrenaline, aerobic respiration, alveoli, aorta, arteries, atrium, blood, blood vessels, bronchi, bronchioles, capillaries, carotid artery, circulatory system, clotting, deoxygenated, diaphragm, gills, haemoglobin, heart, heart rate, intercostal muscles, lungs, oxygenated, plasma, platelets, pulmonary artery, pulmonary vein, pulse, red blood cells, veins, ventricles, white blood cells, wind pipe (trachea)*

Evolution and inheritance: *adaptation, chromosomes, competition, DNA, environmental conditions, environmental variations, evolution, evolutionary change, features, fossil records, genes, genetic variation, inheritance, natural selection, palaeontologist, survival of the fittest, variation over time*

Light (as for Year 3, plus): *absorption, lenses, light source, optics, periscope, prism, rainbow, reflection, refraction, spectrum, transmission*

Electricity (as for Year 4, plus): *circuits, circuit diagrams, components, series circuit, voltage*

A summary of progression and coverage in science topics

	Year 1	Year 2	Year 3	Year 4	Year 5	Year 6
Biology						
Animals, including humans	Identify and name common animals – fish, amphibians, reptiles, birds and mammals. Classify carnivores, herbivores and omnivores. Describe and compare the structure of common animals. Name main body parts.	Animals have offspring that grow into adults. Basic needs of animals and humans. Importance of exercise, diet and hygiene for humans.	Need right type and amount of nutrition. Humans and some animals have skeletons and muscles for support, protection and movement.	Describe simple functions of the human digestive system. Identify different types of teeth and their functions. Construct and interpret food chains.	Describe changes as humans develop from birth to old age.	Identify and name main parts of human circulatory system; describe functions of the heart, blood vessels and blood. Recognise the impact of diet, exercise, drugs and lifestyle on body function. How nutrients and water are transported in animals.
Living things and their habitats		Explore and compare differences between things that are living, dead and never been alive. Things live in habitats to which they are suited. Identify and name plants and animals in their habitats. How animals obtain food from plants and other animals – simple food chain.		Living things can be grouped in a variety of ways. Use classification keys to help group, identify and name a variety of living things. Recognising environments are changing and this can pose dangers to living things.	Describe life cycles of a mammal, an amphibian, an insect and a bird. Describe the life process of reproduction in some plants and animals.	Explain classification of living things into broad groups based on observable characteristics and similarities/differences. Give reasons for classifying plants and animals.
Evolution and inheritance						Fossils provide information about living things that inhabited the Earth millions of years ago. Recognise that living things produce offspring of a similar kind, but they usually vary and aren't identical to their parents. Identify how animals and plants are suited to, and adapt to, their environment.

■SCHOLASTIC

	Year 1	Year 2	Year 3	Year 4	Year 5	Year 6
Biology continued						
Plants	Identify and name common plants, including deciduous and evergreen trees. Identify and describe roots, stem/trunk, leaves, flowers.	Observe and describe how seeds/bulbs grow into plants. Plants need water, light and suitable temperature to grow.	Identify and describe the functions of different parts of flowering plants. Requirements of plants for life and growth and how they vary. Investigate how water is transported in plants. Role of flowers in life cycle of plants.			
Chemistry						
Everyday materials	Distinguish between objects and their materials. Identify and name everyday materials – wood, plastic, glass, metal, water and rock. Describe simple physical properties. Compare and group materials.	(Uses of everyday materials) Identify and compare uses of materials. Changing shape by squashing, bending, twisting and stretching.		(States of matter) Compare and group materials according to their state of matter: solid, liquid, gas. Changing state of some materials when heated/cooled; temperature measurement. Evaporation and condensation in the water cycle; evaporation and temperature.	(Properties and changes of materials) Compare and group together everyday materials based on evidence from fair tests. Understand some materials will dissolve in a liquid to form a solution and how to recover a substance from a solution. Use knowledge of states of matter to decide how mixtures might be separated. Give reasons based on fair tests for particular uses of materials. Demonstrate that dissolving, mixing and changes of state are reversible changes. Some changes result in new materials; changes associated with burning and the action of acid on bicarbonate of soda.	

	Year 1	Year 2	Year 3	Year 4	Year 5	Year 6
			Chemistry continued			
Rocks			Compare and group different kinds of rock from simple physical properties. Describe in simple terms how fossils are formed. Recognise that soils are made from rocks and organic matter.			
			Physics			
Seasonal changes	Observe changes across the seasons. Observe and describe weather and how day length varies.					
Forces and magnets			Movement on different surfaces. Some forces need contact between two objects; some act at a distance. How magnets attract or repel each other and attract some objects but not others. Group materials according to their magnetism. Magnets have two poles. Predict whether two magnets will attract/ repel.		Unsupported objects fall because of gravity between object and the Earth. Effects of drag forces – such as air resistance, water resistance and friction. Mechanical devices such as levers, pulleys and gears, allow a smaller force to have greater effect.	
Light			Light is needed to see things; dark is the absence of light. Light is reflected from surfaces. Sun safety. Associate shadows with a blocked light source. Find patterns that determine shadow size.			Light appears to travel in straight lines. Objects are seen due to giving out light or reflection. Light travels from light sources to our eyes sometimes via an object. Relate light travelling in straight lines to shadow formation.

■ SCHOLASTIC

	Year 1	Year 2	Year 3	Year 4	Year 5	Year 6
						Physics continued
Electricity				Identify electrical appliances. Identify and name parts of a circuit; construct a series circuit. Identify if a lamp will light in a series circuit. Recognise that a switch opens/closes a circuit. Recognise conductors and insulators.		Associate brightness of a lamp or volume of a buzzer with number and voltage of cells used. Compare and give reasons for variations in how components function. Use recognised symbols in a simple circuit diagram.
Earth and space					Describe movement of: Earth relevant to the Sun; the Moon relevant to Earth. Describe the Earth, Moon and Sun as approximately spherical bodies. Earth's rotation explains day/night.	
Sound				Vibrations create sounds. We hear with our ears. Patterns between pitch and features of object producing it. Patterns between volume and strength of vibrations. Sounds get fainter as distance increases.		

Years 1 and 2	Years 3 and 4	Years 5 and 6
	Working scientifically	
Asking simple questions. Observing using simple equipment. Performing simple tests. Identifying and classifying. Using observations and ideas to suggest answers to questions. Gathering and recording data to help answer questions.	Asking relevant questions. Setting up practical enquires, comparatives and fair tests. Making accurate measurements. Gathering, recording, classifying and presenting data. Recording and reporting on findings. Drawing simple conclusions. Identifying observations related to scientific ideas and processes. Using scientific evidence.	Planning enquiries. Taking measurements. Recording data and results. Using test results to make predictions. Reporting and presenting findings. Identifying scientific evidence that has been used to refine ideas.

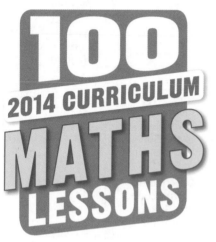
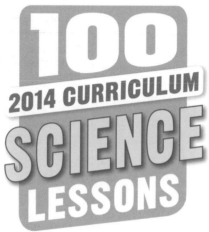